DARDEDEL

Rumi, Hafez
& Love
in New York

a novel-in-verse by
Manoucher Parvin

the permanent press
sag harbor, new york

To My Mother

Copyright© 2003 by Manoucher Parvin

Library of Congress Cataloging-in-Publication Data

Parvin, Manoucher
    Dardedel: Rumi, Hafez & love in New York/by Manoucher
    Parvin
        p. cm.
    ISBN 1-57962-082-5
    1. Jalal al-Da Rama, Maulana, 1207-1273 -- Poetry
    2. oafio, 14th cent. – Poetry. 3. Iranian Americans – Poetry
    4. College Teachers – Poetry 5. Taxicab drivers – Poetry
    6. New York (N.Y.) Poetry. 7. Reincarnation –Poetry
    8. Arizona – Poetry. 9.Deserts – Poetry. 10. Iran – Poetry.
    I. Title

PS3566.A7725 D3 2003
811'.54 – dc21

                                            2002038175

Printed in The United States of America

THE PERMANENT PRESS
4170 Noyac Road
Sag Harbor, NY 11963

Acknowledgments

This would not be the book it is without the support of my dearest friend and colleague Rob Levandoski. He is a wonderful novelist who I must say drinks too much coffee. Time and time again Rob helped me find the right American words for my hard-to-pronounce Persian thoughts.

I am also indebted to these kindred spirits for their critical reading of my novel: Professor Jerry Clinton at Princeton University; Professor Jolita Kavaliunas at The University of Akron; and Professors Fereydoon Family and Franklin Lewis and Ms Julie Sexeny at Emory University. Professor Peter Chelkowski of New York University provided me in English the classic love story of "Layla and Majnun." Mr. Ozzie Bastanjoo of Austin, Texas, my cousin, provided me with the books on Hafez's poetry not available to me.

I also thank Martin and Judith Shepard at The Permanent Press for not only believing in my novel, but believing it could be even better if I worked a little harder. Since he was a freshman in college, my son, now Dr. Ruzbeh Mark Parvin, insisted I should learn how to write on a word processor. He prevailed, and for it I'm a happier, more productive writer. Thank you Ruz.

Finally, I want to thank my parents, Fatemeh Parvin and Mehdi Parvin: Thank you Mother for making me drink my fruit and vegetable juices as a boy—and continuing to remind me about it long distance. I am the feisty professor I am because of your persistent love. And thank you Baba, for never minding my inquisitiveness, for never saying no to my imagination, for never reprimanding me for simply being myself. I wish every boy and girl in the world could have a father like you.

I dedicate this book to the poets of all times and all places,
and to all the lovers of poetry,
who have inspired me to dardedel in poems.

To Rachelle

with thanks for your
interest in my work.

I hope this Novel will
take you to places
where stars learn to shine
where it took me as
I imagined, & wrote it.

M. Parvin

330 666 4347
MPARVIN @ adelphia.net

Introduction

Do you know this Persian word, *dardedel*?

In English we would call it a heart-to-heart talk, yet a dardedel is so much more than heart to heart, and so much more than talk.

Darde means ache. *Del* means heart. But put together they mean *one* and *another* sharing the most private, sincere and important things. Dardedel unchains us from the burdens of our isolation and loneliness. By uniting our soul with another soul, our deepest thoughts and feelings are set free, without the shame of judgment or the fear of betrayal. It is this absolute trust that makes dardedel so special and so sacred.

This book called *Dardedel* is my dardedel with you.

So may I tell you a little about me? Before you join Professor Pirooz on his magical American adventure?

I was about to enter elementary school, in Iran, in the tumultuous 1940s, when I first began watching and listening to my father and his friends drinking wine, feasting on nuts and fruit, smoking opium, and talking about everything—a collective dardedel in the sanctuary of our big house.

His guests were philosophers and poets, writers and musicians, businessmen and scientists, politicians and Sufi Dervishes. They had one thing in common: their hearts reaching for other hearts, fusing into one big heart; and their minds ready to learn from other minds, fusing into one big mind.

I remember it so well, all these years and miles away. They laughed and even cried together. It was the first time I saw grown men weeping with no death in the family. From them I learned that it was possible to talk with friends with no reservation or inhibition at all. I would go on to attend many schools and earn many degrees, but this school in my father's house was the first and most important—and I have yet to graduate from it!

So I inhaled the science talk, the Sufi poems and songs, the mysterious chit-chat about love and sex. I watched the Dervishes twirl and inhaled the drifting smoke, and felt high as I grew and understood more and more. I exhaled my innocence, my boyish notions of how the world is, or should be.

Do not think I was an unnoticed Persian fly on the wall. My father was quite conscious of my presence. Like the King of Serendip sending his sons into the world to complete their educations, my father was bringing me into his world, to *begin* mine.

As for the opium smoking, please remember the time and the place. It was quite fashionable and the world had yet to learn the dangers of second-hand smoke!

Before fully appreciating these fantastic gatherings of learned men, I found myself on a propeller plane flying to America, to learn modern science. I had set aside my own ambitions in literature to do what my country needed me to do. I was so young and idealistic then.

In America I studied hard and, still in my twenties, wrote a book on electronics. But I soon retired from the formal pursuit of the hard sciences. The answers to human problems were not to be found there.

Meanwhile, I joined those toiling for human rights, for democracy in Iran, and for civil rights in the United States. With youthful exuberance we were in a big hurry to make the world a better place. Ha-ha! How wonderfully optimistic we were!

Soon I was at Columbia University, in New York City, a graduate student in economics. Within two years I was teaching economics there! As the years passed, I would write in many social science fields, although interdisciplinary study was not yet appreciated as it is today. I had learned from my father and his friends not to be inhibited or restricted by those horse blinders called *specialization*. I was thirsty for answers. I would plunge into any subject my heart desired, irrespective of professional disapproval. I felt an obligation to feed my hungriest urges and curiosities.

As time passed, I realized that the answers provided by the social sciences were not enough for me. It was time for me to return to my original love, the study of the human soul. I began writing novels to investigate my soul, the souls of others, and the soul of history. And I began to write poems. Persians feel at home in poems.

As I climbed the academic ladder I felt emptier at each rung. Emptiness, like a cancer of the soul, invaded me, established roots in me, and grew in me. I know now that the multitudes of Americans seeking refuge in Hafez and Rumi, and the other mystic poets of Iran, also suffer from this same spiritual emptiness. And, of course, Hafez and Rumi had arrived in New York to rescue lost souls long before I resurrected them in this book!

All told, this work has been a healing effort—a dardedel free of all literary restriction, personal fears and pretensions, a dardedel where science and spirituality clash, where modernity and history clash, where the soul of man is mended, if only on paper temporarily.

Perhaps you have never heard of the old Persian poets Hafez and Rumi.

Jalalad-Din Rumi's life spanned most of the thirteenth century, 1207 to 1273. He was a poet, philosopher and mystic, often referred to as Mowlana, which means *our master*. For many years he followed in his father's footsteps as a conservative theologian, teaching at a religious school in the city of Konya. Then a Sufi mystic from Tabriz named Shamsal-Din (*Sun of the Faith*) wandered into his life.

Rumi recalled his encounter with Shams thus:

> I was dead, I was resurrected
> I was tears, I was turned into laughter
> The majesty, the love, came upon me
> And crowned me with immortality.

So, Rumi spent almost all of his time with Shams, neglecting his family and his work. It is said that Rumi's jealous students secretly murdered Shams. More likely, Shams left so Rumi could find his own path in life. Regardless, Sham's influence changed the grieving Rumi's life.

The tragedy of Rumi became a wonderful gift for man. Collected into two books, The *Divan-e Shams* and the *Masnavi*, Rumi's poems are mystical and moral discourses with his community. They have illuminated the soul of humankind for centuries. In December 1999, *Time* magazine named Rumi "Mystic of the Century." His works continue to sell in astonishing numbers and are recorded by celebrities, including the Material Girl, Madonna! His ideas also have attracted many psychoanalytic therapists in America.

One more thing about the Mowlana: He is credited with founding the Sufi sect called the Mevlevis, which gave the world those fantastic, spiraling prayer-dancers Westerners know as Whirling Dervishes.

Now, about Hafez: He was born in 1320, some fifty years after Rumi's death. His real name was Shamsal-Din Muhammad. Hafez means *one who remembers*. It is said he knew the Koran by heart.

Little is known about his life, except that he most likely received a classical Islamic education and practiced Sufism. Unlike so many writers of his time, whose deaths preceded their fame, Hafez's poems caught fire almost as soon as he wrote them. By the time he did die in 1390, he was loved by many and despised by a few. Today he is famous throughout the world. Some of the greatest Western writers, Johann Wolfgang von Goethe among them, have considered themselves among his students. He is called Prince of Poets or Poet of Poets by some American literary critics.

Hafez explored various poetic forms. *Divan-e Hafez* is a dazzling collection of poems on love, liberty, drunkenness, nature, spiritual devotion and ascendance, injustice and hypocrisy. Unlike the wise and relatively proper Rumi, Hafez was something of a literary and anticlerical rascal. You will catch the differences as you read my dardedel. And you will see that I am worse than a rascal!

Anyway, Hafez spent almost all of his life in the city of Shiraz. He is buried in a mausoleum there.

A few quick words about Sufism: The roots of this mystical movement are older than Islam. Zoroastrianism, Buddhism and the Judeo-Christian mysticisms are all tributaries of Sufism. It came into full flower, however, as Islam spread across the Persian empire. Sufism derives from the word for wool—*suf*—and refers to the woolen gowns worn by early Muslim ascetics.

By the 11th century there were Sufi schools or gathering places, *Khâneghâh,* all over Iran. *Khâne* means "home" and *ghâh* means "the moment." Together they could mean living the moment, being fully conscious of the moment/reality. Sufis believe that self-knowledge and deep intuition are vital means for knowing, for spiritual ascendance and self-realization. Even the lowliest person can experience the ultimate reality or God directly in his or her heart. An objective self-evaluation of abilities and intentions, which sufism promotes, enhances a sufi's chances of survival in any situation.

Beyond its spiritual dimension and consciousness examining, retraining and revitalizing, Sufism has played an important, even decisive, role in Persian literature, music, and art. Today it is even the foundation of a major approach to psychotherapy in the United States.

I like the permission Sufism gives me to figure out the world for myself and reach for *vasal.* Vasal is a Persian word meaning fruition and unity— the unity of lovers, the unity of the faithful with God, unity with a most cherished dream by realizing that dream.

Dardedel is written entirely in verse, in honor of Hafez and Rumi and the other epic poets of my homeland. To translate them, I drink their poems until I am intoxicated, then I assume my American identity and write down what I'm experiencing. Hafez and Rumi would have composed in free verse today.

Consider my book a Persian dish cooked in America:

There is a pinch of Eastern culture and mysticism,
A dash of tenderness resurrected from industrial ashes,
A touch of science and technology related to the fate of man,
Drops of liquid soul from Hafez and Rumi,
Blended with the love story of all love stories,
Into a poem of poems, and,
I pray, a dardedel of self-realization between you and me.

I realize that I am an accented noise in America. I speak with an accent. I think with an accent. I feel, love, dream, and write with an accent. I am an accent. And I will die an accent. I've accepted this condition about myself. Dear reader, please do the same.

I have started our dardedel with a love poem—expressing my love for the ascended men and women of the distant future. I dedicate it to you.

My Love Song Of Love Songs

I kiss the blossoms of spring—it is you.
I kiss the magic of autumn—it is you.
I splash in the womb of summer—it is you.
I swim across the ice of winter.
To find you,
To hug you,
To love you.
All things lovable are you.

I love the song of Hafez—it is you.
I understand the wisdom of Rumi—it is you.
I practice the Zen of Buddha—it is you.
I admire the science of Einstein—it is you.
I dance to the music of Mozart—it is you.
I breathe in the blue of Picasso,
When remembering you, when missing you,
You, lovable you.

You are the perfect mother and the perfect father.
You are the perfect lover, the perfect ascended soul,
The supreme good humankind should be,
That men and women, once perfected, will be.
I long for you, keep vigil for you,
Forever, until I am no longer.

MANOUCHER PARVIN

BOOK ONE:

The Unimaginable

1 Dardedel With New Friends

Tonight Professor Pirooz flies to Phoenix,
From New York where he's taught for so many years.
He has no luggage, no return ticket,
He just has himself and the ache in his heart.
At the airport he flags a taxi,
And to the sleepy brown cabby says,
"Take me to the desert they call the Sonora,
To that endless world where the tall saguaros grow."
The cabby studies the handsome stranger's sad chocolate eyes.
"At two in the morning, sir?"
"If that's what time it is," answers Professor Pirooz.
"It's a long drive," warns the cabby.
"I have plenty of time," says Pirooz.
"It'll cost you a pretty penny," adds the cabby.
"I have plenty of pennies, too," says Professor Pirooz.

So the sleepy brown cabby drives him deep into the Sonora,
On a road hardly driven, not even by day.
"Stop here," says Pirooz, surveying the nothingness full of things.
"You're the boss," says the cabby, his foot squeezing the brake.
Pirooz pays his fare, waves good-bye and starts walking,
The sleepy brown cabby drives away.

Professor Pirooz has come to the Sonora to sing a song—
A song without sound, or words, or predictable notes.
He has come to sing this song in a palace of his imagination,
An endless desert palace without doors, walls, roofs, or floors,

14

A palace full of reptiles, bats, red ants, cactuses, and coyote,
All like him, thirsty, longing for a raindrop of salvation.

Yes, Pirooz has come to the Sonora to die,
To let the blazing sun rob him of his memory and
To let thirst and hunger finish him off.
And so he trudges the hard-soft sand toward a hill,
Toward two tall saguaros, standing side by side in the night.

Falling to his knees before these bony, silent cactuses, he says:
"I am a refugee tonight,
With two new friends whose arms stretch to the unknown.
Ask me not why I'm in this otherworldly place alone,
Thinking of death—my death.
Ask me not about causes and consequences,
Or other imponderable questions.
But ask me what I want and I will tell you that I am starved,
As you are perhaps starved, to be loved and listened to,
Just like the canaries who scream from their fancy cages,
Just like the homeless who scream from their cardboard boxes."

"My dear saguaros," Pirooz confesses,
"I need to dardedel with you tonight.
Do you know this beautiful word, *dardedel?*
Dardedel is soul talk, wound talk, and joy talk, to a kindred spirit.
It is embracing vulnerability without fear of judgment or shame.
It is confiding to stars who glow with understanding and never tell.
It is one soul uniting with another, freeing both, enriching both.
I sucked dardedel with my mother's milk,
Back in Persia, long ago, where the word was invented.
Back in Persia, long ago, where the word invented me."

"So now listen to me," Pirooz begs,
"As you would listen to a somber cello:

My home has disappeared behind years of exile,
I can barely mourn for losses I can barely recall.
My mother tongue has been conquered, word by word by English,
So that I have neither one language nor two, but two halves.
My two homes are at war, tearing my mind and heart apart.
I am a teacher dedicated to teaching truth,
Yet I am afraid to teach the truths I know,
For fear I may lose my welcome, even my job
So I must teach the Norm, the damn Norm,
As if it was the word of God.
I must dissimulate, dissimulate, dissimulate,
To no end, until I am a foreigner even to myself,
Until I'm an accent even to myself.
That is why I've come to your desert, my dear saguaros,
To die and be myself."

Cries Professor Pirooz: "Yes! Yes! I am despairing.
I am despairing that we humans, once such happy monkeys,
No longer make love, but make death,
With our endless copulating we sew and sew
An enormous quilt under which we will suffocate
From the poisons our sheer numbers spew
So that the more of us, the less of us, until there are none of us.
I remember the lovemate I thought would be with me forever,
Buried breastless from cancer.
I see frogs born with no limbs, eagles without eyes or wings.
I see men of Science grinding daisies into bombs,
Children pouring honey into molds for bullets.
I see men of God, killing God's dreams, with God's own words.
I see my willpower wavering, that my warnings are nothing,
Piled on nothing, changing nothing.
So I am ready to be nothing before I am nothing, to die before I die."
Exhausted by his lament, Pirooz now gazes at the twin saguaros,
Silhouetted against a magnificent moon,

As stars by the billions twinkle their existence.
He is intoxicated by the solitude, by the unity with all things,
Even with the Pinacate beetles,
That when offended can be as stinky as a skunk.
He asks the two cactuses towering over him, "Did you hear me?"
Pirooz is not expecting an answer,
Not an answer his ears can hear, anyway.
But his ears do hear, as the taller of the two saguaros says:
"Yes, we heard you, Pirooz.
The moon and the sand and the bats heard you, too."
Then the shorter one says:
"But the question is, Pirooz, do you hear yourself?"
Pirooz is astounded, terrified and paralyzed,
As if facing a gargantuan pair of multi-headed green cobras.
He falls desert silent, trembling, sweating, despite the night cold.
Finally recovering, he somehow finds the courage to ask:
"How is it that plants speak without mouths or tongues?
How is it you know my name?"

The taller saguaro chuckles softly, asking,
"How is it you talk to *cactuses*? When you don't know *their* names?"
Pirooz shrugs like his students shrug.
"I never knew that cactuses had names."
Now both saguaros chuckle, and the shorter one says:
"And we have never met anyone who talks to cactuses—
Certainly no one named Pirooz!"
The professor ventures a sheep's smile. "It is a Persian name."
Growls the taller saguaro: "We know it is a Persian name.
And we know what it means—one who is victorious!
Which apparently you are not!"
"Right," answers Pirooz, almost sobbing, "Which apparently I am not."

The saguaros wait for the professor to say something more,
To complain some more, to explain some more.

17

But he just sits there,
With a melancholic grin on his melancholic face,
Whispering a song to himself without words or music.
Finally the taller saguaro leans forward, without bending its back.
"You asked us to dardedel, which surprised and delighted us.
But now you sit there like the other stones,
Neither asking nor telling—only disappointing."

Pirooz asks their forgiveness with a pilgrim's bow:
"I was expecting you only to listen, but then you started to talk.
So to tell you the truth, my tongue is flabbergasted into silence."
The saguaros seem to look at each other without twisting,
Seem to agree without nodding.
The taller one says: "We are flabbergasted, too,
To find a Persian in an American desert,
Dardedelling with cactuses as if they were old friends.
Pirooz! You say you wish to open your heart,
Asking from us no more than to listen.
Even when cut into pieces, trees listen!
That is what trees do best—listen and listen!
But when a man opens his heart, he opens other hearts, too,
Does he not, Pirooz?"
The professor nods and nods: "Yes, that is dardedel."
Pirooz feels the saguaros embrace him,
Even though their stiff arms have not moved.
The taller one says: "Speak Pirooz, sparing no sin or secret,
Out with everything! Confession without fear!"
"Yes! Yes!" sings Pirooz. "Yes! Yes! Without fear!"

Joy pours from the saguaros' leathery pores,
And the shorter one says: "Then I confess that my name is Hafez!"
Pirooz covers his dry lips with his sweaty fingertips:
"That is the pen name of Shamsal-Din Muhammad,
The great poet of my homeland, Iran.

18

One who remembers, Hafez means,
One whose heart holds every word of the Koran.
A cactus named after an old Persian poet. Just imagine!"
The saguaro named Hafez moonglows with joy:
"Not only is my name Hafez—I am Hafez!"
Before Pirooz can ask the hows and whys bubbling inside him,
The taller saguaro says: "And I confess that they call me Mowlana!"
Pirooz squeals with astonishment: "Mowlana, The Master,
The name of respect given Jalalad-Din Rumi—"
The taller cactus laughs loud:
"Yes, Pirooz! Just as Hafez is really Hafez, I am really Rumi,
The other old poet you were forced to memorize as a boy!"
"Forced but gladly so," Pirooz insists. "Forced but gladly so!"

And so they dardedel,
This mortal man who wants to leave this world,
These two wise spirits stuck in hot American sand,
Uprooted and reborn, like so many Persian immigrants in exile.
"So," asks Pirooz of them, "Just why are you here?"
Answers Rumi: "We are counting the stars."
Pirooz is puzzled: "Of all eternity's pleasures you choose to count stars?"
Hafez shrugs. "No one knows how many stars there are."
"But that is not true," the professor protests,
"Astronomers have estimated that there are—"
Rumi interrupts him: "God's handiwork is not for estimating,
It is for knowing!"
Pirooz is defiant: "I would not waste my time
Counting the uncountable."
Then he takes a second to cool his anger, and with a grin says,
"Who knows! Perhaps the stars are themselves counting cactuses!
Perhaps they are just like people, prone to count everything!"
Rumi reminds him that he and Hafez are transcendent souls,
With toes rooted in the hot sands of eternity,

Unrestricted and unseduced by mortal time.
"We have no time to waste, and all time to waste," he says.
"Still, we must pass time and watch time pass us.
And if after we have counted these stars,
And we have discovered nothing more than their number,
We will at least know that."

Pirooz smiles, thinking he has them:
"Though their light still wanders in space,
Many of those stars no longer exist!
So you will end up with worse than an estimate,
You will end up with a sum that's incorrect!"

It is Rumi's turn to smile: "Hafez and I are in America.
Are we, or are we not, in America?
Are we not nothing but the ancient lights of our mortal selves?"
Pirooz sighs, and concedes: "Yes, if you and Hafez are standing here,
And still enlightening hearts and minds,
Then the stars are there, too, whether they actually are or not."
Pirooz now grins, and half seriously says,
"Perhaps when I am dead I will come and help you count."

But Rumi shows no enthusiasm for his offer:
"God wills both birth and death, and
God forbids murder, even if inflicted by self upon self.
Has God not made that clear from the start, Pirooz?"
The mortal professor shrugs, saying: "Search the Holy Books
And you will find that God is forever granting man free will
But forever snatching it away when man tries to use it."
There is a smile on Rumi's face now,
Though it is not a smile of happiness.
It is a smile of wisdom.
He says: "I see that you are not a man easily impressed, Pirooz,
With chiseled stone or scribbled parchments rolled tight.

I see that you are a Modern Man!
We had modern men in my time, too.
I was one of them myself, in fact."

Pirooz understands only too well what the old Sufi means.
"Unfortunately, the modern man thinks that almost
All important things are already discovered—by himself."

Rumi's prickly face does not show it, but he is delighted:
"Not bad for a mortal, Pirooz!
But what I want you to understand is more weighty than that!
What I want you to understand is this:
A new day, a new night, a new garden, a new garden path.
A new thought and an old question resolved.
A new happiness and a new fatigue.
With each breath the world becomes new!
And we become new!
But in death one misses all which becomes new.
In death one misses using all he once knew.
Why is it, Pirooz, that you are tired of counting stars as a mortal?
Yet you wish to count them as a dead man?
Do you think the truths on our side
Are more true than the truths on your side?"
Pirooz is suddenly stricken by this question,
His mouth as wide as a cavern full of bats. "They are not?"

Rumi is stern, yet loving to the professor:
"Why would we be standing here as stiff thirsty saguaros,
Painstakingly counting stars if we knew how many there were?
You scoff at the Holy Books, yet God forbids suicide for a reason.
He gave you life not as a punishment—but to sense His intentions.
He gave you eyes not just for crying—but also to see and discover.
He gave you ears not just to hear—but to listen and understand.
He gave you a tongue not just to talk—but to taste and inform.

21

He gave you fingers not to poke and demand—
But to touch and love others with."

Without lifting his cactus arms, Rumi beckons Pirooz to his side.
"This is why you must not take your life.
This is why you must endure your exile—with patience.
Why you must endure the fools who persecute you—with patience.
Why you must continue to teach and be taught—with patience.
Live on with patience, Pirooz! Live on with hope, Pirooz!
Death will come soon enough, Pirooz!
When you started this dardedel with us,
You said that you must die before you die.
Professor! You must live before you live!"

Just then the black desert sky is sliced by a knife of fire.
"Another star to subtract," Hafez sighs.
"That is not a star," says Pirooz. "That is merely a meteor,
A piece of cold rock sucked from space by gravitation."
Hafez is disheartened. "Not a star? Are you sure?
We have been subtracting them by the millions."
"It is just a rock," says Pirooz, "Not much bigger perhaps
Than the pebble we are standing on."
"Are you sure that you are sure?" asks Hafez.
Rumi pats Hafez on the shoulder.
"We must listen to this modern man.
He knows and knows that he knows—
Just as we once knew and knew that we knew!"

And so their dardedel turns to talk of the Universe:
To talk of Genesis and the genesis of Science.
To truths unprovable, to lies unassailable.
Finally Rumi asks: "In what truths, professor, do you believe?"
Pirooz looks up at the exploding stars and declares:

"In the beginning was Hell, and the Hell was a raging ball of fire,
Ignited by a big, big bang,
Exploding into an emptiness that had no ears or ends,
Flashing into a big darkness that had no eyes, mind, or heart,
Becoming a dark existence that had no consciousness.
And later this raging existence jettisoned stars just like sparks,
And this sputtering dust was congealed by gravity into worlds,
One of them our own Earth, pirouetting forever in luminosity.
And the Earth, impregnated by light, presented the universe a child,
And soon this child stood up and questioned everything in sight,
Filling the lonely air with words and more words,
Creating a new self with tools, art, science, and a relentless curiosity.
Soon prophets appeared to reveal the intentions of myriad gods.
Holding high their Holy Books, they taught right from wrong,
Confirming Good and Evil in the Spirit of Man.
But their messages were conflicting and unsubstantiated,
Filling man not with reason but with hatred, doubt, and fear,
Forcing him to kill and kill in the name of the phantom gods."

"Yes! Yes!" Hafez interjects, reminded of his own poem:

"Go ahead, and rationalize
The war of seventy-two nations.
Since they did not see the truth
They pursued only false tales."

Pirooz, eyes closed, continues: "Incubated in the minds of mortals,
Little by little the many little gods united into one big God,
Invisible but existing everywhere, omniscient and omnipotent,
Even in the vacuum of space presumably.
Exclaims Rumi: "Hell first, Creation next, God last?"
Pirooz nods vigorously: "And then man abandoned
This unhelpful God in favor of Science and Money."
Asks Rumi: "And you, Pirooz? You are one of these people?"

23

Answers Pirooz: "I am a product of my time, Mowlana,
Though the money part has never enchanted me much."

Rumi ponders Pirooz's words, both moved and unmoved by them.
Finally he asks: "Is not your Big Bang a story, too?
Just like the Holy Scriptures you dismiss?"
"Of course it is a story," Pirooz admits.
"But Genesis and Science are not equal stories.
Science is proven or disproven all the time,
While the scriptures claim beauty, truth, and morality for all time."
Rumi looks deep into Pirooz with his invisible cactus eyes.
"Science discerns only the form of things, the properties of objects,
Creating only a painting of what the senses sense.
But for true understanding don't we need God?"
Pirooz retorts: "Science is about facts and the search for truth,
Religion is about values and the search for meaning.
There is one science, but many faiths.
If the many faiths could unite into one,
And just prescribe values instead of claiming truth,
Then Science and faith not only could coexist,
But blend and peacefully co-inhabit the soul of Man."
Hafez is enjoying this debate between
The Sufi master and the man of Science.
He says to Pirooz: "This Big Bang story of yours is a good one,
Yet it leaves as many unanswered questions
As does the Big God story Rumi and I were taught.
If the Universe began with a bang, why?
And where and what was the Universe before the bang?
And how long did it simmer before banging, and
Why not many big bang bangs in the empty blue, and a Multiverse?"
Pirooz has wondered these things himself, of course,
And knows he cannot begin to answer Hafez.
He can do nothing but laugh at his own ignorance, and say:
"Do you have to make trouble even when you are a cactus, Hafez?"

24

2 The God of Random Intelligence

Having defended Science with such stubbornness and such zeal,
Pirooz realizes he also has been defending himself,
His generation, and his time.
So when Rumi asks him if he still wishes to die,
Pirooz is embarrassed by his uncertainty.
"I am prepared to die here, just as before," he says.
"Still I am equally prepared to go on living."
"Well, you had better decide quickly," says Hafez,
"Before the first star ever counted—the sun—rises and bakes
Both you and your ambivalence, caring not one tiny pistachio nut
Whether you want to be baked or not."
Pirooz, not knowing west from east, twirls like a Dervish,
Searching the horizon for a telling sliver of light.
"I don't know," he cries, "I don't know, I don't know!
But I must wake up before I can never wake up!"

Rumi makes Pirooz an offer: "If you cannot decide to live or to die,
Then you have already decided to live, if only for a few more days.
Go home to New York, Pirooz, to your students and your life.
For while your decision to die is sincere,
The depth of your sincerity remains in question.
So struggle on, Pirooz, struggle on for at least another year."
"A year?" protests Pirooz. "A year is a long time to suffer!"
Says Rumi: "A year of suffering is nothing
Compared to an eternity of regret."
"That's true enough," says Pirooz.
"But what if I still want to die after that year is over?"
"Go home for one year, Pirooz," Hafez answers.

"And then return to the desert if you still wish to die.
We will then sing the old Persian songs to you,
To numb your pain while the sun does its job."
"And what," asks Pirooz, "if I have decided to live?"
Says Rumi: "Then that will be the beginning of a new poem,
And we will recite it together, in your presence or absence."

So Pirooz agrees—who is he to refuse Rumi or Hafez?—
And the dardedel ends.
The moon is fading and one by one the stars are turning their backs.

Just as a sliver of sunlight turns the black mountains pink,
Rumi opens his leathery side,
And lets Pirooz drink his fill of the milk inside.
"To renew you for your long walk," The Mowlana says.
Then, Hafez throws down his right cactus arm,
And when it lands at Pirooz's feet it is a beautiful green umbrella.
"To shade you, professor," Hafez says.

Pirooz does not want to leave but knows he must.
"I am so glad the cactuses I chose were you," he says.
"And we are glad that you were you!" answers Hafez.
"Yes," adds Rumi. "At first we thought you were a cactus thief coming,
One of those terrible men with ropes and shovels,
Who steal plants from the desert where they have always belonged
For tiny plots in the city where they will never belong."
"I have never been good with shovels or ropes," says Pirooz.

As Pirooz walks from the hill toward the road,
He hears Rumi's voice booming behind him, telling him a story,
A story Pirooz remembers reading in Iran:

It is a story about a Bedouin woman,
Camping in the desert with her husband.

She complains to him about their poverty, saying:
"Everyone is happy and prosperous except us!
We have no bread. We have no spices. We have no water jug . . ."
She goes on, complaining and complaining.
"If God is abundant, we must be following an impostor."
The husband listens until he can listen no more.
"Woman" he scolds, "this poverty is my deepest joy.
This bare way of life is honest and beautiful.
We can hide nothing when we're like this . . ."

Finally at dawn Professor Pirooz reaches Phoenix,
His face filthy with sand and sweat.
He washes in a fountain, in the center of the city,
While children laugh and mothers glare.
Refreshed, he hurries to the airport
And slides his credit card to the freckly girl at the counter.
"One ticket to New York City, please."
"Going home?" she asks.
"Not home, but where I live," he answers.

On the plane he nibbles his precious bag of peanuts,
Looking down at the slow retreating earth,
Wondering if his night in the desert had been real or a dream.
Did he really dardedel with Hafez and Rumi?
How could it be?
Jalalad-Din Rumi had lived eight centuries ago, Hafez fully seven,
When Islam, a hearty vine with beautiful flowers,
Was spreading across the dark world, bridging East and West.
How, now, so many centuries later, could they be alive,
Standing side by side in the Sonora counting stars?
Of course it was a dream, induced by his exhausted body and mind,
Or an hallucination induced by intoxicating spores adrift in the air.
But what about this umbrella? He did not buy this umbrella.

Hafez fashioned it from his arm, and gave it to him,
To shade him on his journey beneath the unrelenting sun.
So it was not a dream, Pirooz realizes, and not an hallucination.
Hafez and Rumi were really real.
But why did they reveal themselves to him?
Was it just the coincidence of their meeting that led them to speak?
Was that all it was, a random encounter explainable by physical laws?
Did fate send him there,
To those two magnificent giants, to save him from himself?
Did Hafez and Rumi know he was coming?
Or were they as surprised as he?
Pirooz cradles the green umbrella—the beautiful umbrella
With the handle carved from smooth Persian oak.
The tines are cast from strong Persian brass.
The canopy is woven of soft Persian silk.

His life in New York is so hard, so insidiously hideous and absurd.
He is trapped on an island seething with lost immigrant souls,
Surrounded by dead rivers carrying dead fish.
"Welcome stranger," Mother Liberty says,
Holding high her torch so the stranger can see,
"Now forget who and what you were,
Forget the mountains and the waving poppies,
Forget your language and your customs,
Forget your ancestors and your memories and your dreams.
Conform, repent, melt into the melting pot,
And dream an American dream.
You wanted to come, now become what we want you to become."
Says Pirooz to himself: "Life is difficult but give it another year!"

The little bag of peanuts empties much too quickly.
Pirooz licks the salt from his lips
And asks the man in the blue suit next to him for paper and a pen.
The blue-suited man is annoyed by Pirooz's request,

Annoyed by Pirooz's accent,
Annoyed by the green umbrella poking his elbow.
But the blue-suited man is a wise traveler,
Understanding from too many years on airplanes and trains
That the best way to deal with an annoying stranger
Is to give him what he wants.
So he opens his briefcase and hands Pirooz
An entire tablet and three sharp pencils.

"Thank you," says Pirooz with a smile and a tip of his head.
"Don't mention it," says the man,
Warning Pirooz with his gruff voice
That the pad and pencils were not a gift but a bribe,
Warning him that he was *not* to mention it again,
Warning him that he was not to mention *anything* again.
The blue-suited man closes his eyes and feigns sleep.
And Professor Pirooz begins to write this poem:

Death is the last love, the final kiss.
Death is the last gift, the end of hypocrisy.
Death is freedom, in numberless forms in limitless times.
Death is a friend, helping with your vexing chores.
Death is a bath in honey, sweetening bitter things.
Death cures all ills, pays your bills, frees you from fear,
And even brightens the days of your enemies—
Who seem always to grow in numbers.
Death is a rose, red and supple in the vase of time,
Never wilting, never perfuming but sniffed by all.
Death is a song with an endless beat.
Death is resurrection, into unknown colors, scents, sights.
Death is the heaven of heretics, martyrs, and the starved.
Death is a beginning with no middle to savor, or end to fear.
Death is a bittersweet chocolate bar that grows in your hand.
Death is an orgasm that never ends.

Death is a subterranean star, nourishing worms and baking bones.
I wish you knew that Death is beautiful, I wish Death knew it, too.
I wish we sang Happy Deathday just as we sing the birthday song,
And I wish that Death would let me save a few days of life,
In reserve, for future use, so that
I could claim a day every thousand years or so,
To quench my unrelenting curiosity of what will be,
To answer my unanswered questions, such as, why . . .

As Professor Pirooz writes,
A flight attendant with red-cherry lips interrupts him,
Asking, "Macaroni or chicken?"
He replies: "When it was alive,
The chicken couldn't fly this far.
So how is it that it flies so high now, without wings to flap?"
"The macaroni then, sir?" asks the attendant.
"Whatever," answers Pirooz.

Pirooz eats his macaroni, and watches the blue-suited man eat his.
The earth below them is carpeted with cotton clouds and
The sun is dancing on the airplane's silver wings.
Pirooz leans toward the blue-suited man and whispers:
"I have decided that it is better to be alive and
Eating macaroni high above the ground,
Than to be dead and eating my regrets below the ground."
The blue-suited man gives Pirooz his fancy pen.

Though the plane flies faster than the fastest hummingbird,
The hours inside the plane creep as slowly as the slowest turtle.
Yawning one yawn after another, Pirooz wishes that God
Were more generous with His secrets,
Wishes that instead of letting his inquisitive children
Struggle for answers with their cumbersome imaginations,

He would simply appear one day,
And tell them the hows and whys of Everything,
So that his children could give up their arguments,
Their silliness and their superstitions,
Their hating and their jealousies and their wars.
Why, Pirooz wonders, yawning and yawning,
Why didn't God just make Heaven and leave it at that?
Why all these planets and stars and unanswered questions?

Now Pirooz is sound asleep, and dreaming.
He is alone in a square white room without corners,
And though the ceiling is a mile high, he must bow his head.
The floor is invisible but hard.
He hears someone knocking at a door on the ceiling,
A door that a second ago was not there.
The knock is unobtrusive but compelling—the music of fate.
Pirooz puts his hand on the golden knob and turns.
"Professor," voices say. "May we come in to dardedel some more?"
Pirooz pulls the door open, saying, "Yes, please! Come in! Come in!"

But it is not Hafez and Rumi standing there, not as he expected.
It is a single stranger, floating in a rainbow of light.
"Guess who?" asks the stranger.
Being an unbeliever, Pirooz cries out with dread, "Oh, my God! God!"

"You are forgiven for not believing in me, Pirooz!" says God.
"Worse is a pretentious believer than a sincere unbeliever.
So be secure and hear my lamentation,
And then carry it exactly, Pirooz, to the heart of mankind."
"I will," promises Pirooz. "I will! I will!"
And so God begins: "You people of this world,
You puny creatures of mine,
You undo my doings by all means conceivable,
Until you are no longer in my image, but an image I never imagined!

31

You fly though I gave you no wings.
You dive deep though I gave you no fins.
You invent telescopes—to see beyond my intent.
You invent microscopes—seeing things I wanted hidden.
You eavesdrop on space, on times and things long gone.
You force rivers into beds I never approved of.
And you seed clouds to thunder and cry
On the barren fields where I sent them to rest.
You poison the earth and heat the earth,
Until you have made a hell of earth.
You kill the unborn I wanted born,
And force birth upon others against my will.
You prolong dying for profit, torturing the sick with heartless machines.
You make vaccines and fabricate atom bombs,
Confusing my Angel of Death,
Who in turn pesters me, asking:
'Why have you allowed this creature to kill my plagues,
While permitting him to make bombs more powerful than me?'
And I, embarrassed, must answer: 'Allowed? Permitted?
Man stopped asking my permission long ago.'"
God falls silent now, his narrow eyes searching Pirooz's wide ones.
Pirooz does not know what to say, or if he should say anything at all.
Finally he offers this: "What, God, can I say?
We think of things to do and then we do them."
God offers no clue whether this was a good answer or a bad one.
He simply continues: "You scar the face of the earth
With boundaries, barbed and deadly, and wage war over them.
You tramp on the moon's surface,
My creation to inspire poets to compose.
And you remain restless even on the Sabbath Day.
You *extinct* what I intend to *exist!*
Not only birds and fishes and helpless plants,
But my prophets, and even Me!
With this Science of yours, this psychology and philosophy of yours.

You erode my words in the Holy Books,
As if I am the mud and you the rain, and not the other way around!"

Extinct is not a verb, Pirooz thinks,
But then who is he to question God's English?
He does however, question His wisdom:
"If you didn't want us to act this way, why did you create us this way?"
Answers God: "I intentionally willed myself
Not to know in advance if you would use
The potential I embodied in you to go against my will.
I wondered—yes, I wonder, too, if I wish—
How you, my sole random intelligence,
Would co-exist with the other things I created.
But you make peace with nothing, not even yourselves."

Pirooz is surprised to hear such a scientific phrase
Tumble from the Creator's lips:
"Random intelligence? What, Almighty God, is that?"
God, sensing Pirooz's astonishment, smiles and continues:
"Man is unpredictable, acting under feuding influences and intentions
Just like a game of Backgammon, which
You Persians invented to mirror the human condition,
Where intelligence and luck, intention and fate, interact."

As God falls silent, as if for eternity,
Pirooz fidgets and says: "Surely you knew we might be trouble."
God answers him: "The universe is my self-realization.
I created the Random Intelligence—The creature you call Man—
To foreclose any thought of Me as an absolute despot,
Who consults no one and pre-determines everything,
Preempting any question or criticism forever.
So, in short, Man is a serendipitous response to my creation."
"May I say something foolish?" asks Pirooz.
God is amused: "No one has stopped your foolishness yet, Pirooz!

Say as many foolish things as you like!"
Pirooz feels himself blushing. "Just a couple will do, starting with this:
Why is every creature you make a lemon?"
"A lemon?" asks God.
Pirooz explains himself: "What I mean is this,
Everything you make seems to have a defect or two."

"No one is perfect," answers God solemnly.
Pirooz is sympathetic toward this imperfect, dardedelling God,
Saying, "Perhaps you, Almighty God,
Should create a supervisor, and report your failures to him,
So that someday only those lemons
Intended to be lemons will be lemons!"

God falls into His unbounded silence,
So Pirooz continues: "So what do you intend to do to us,
Or with us, those of us who are upsetting your grand designs?"
Now God does reply, His voice as sharp as the thunderbolts
That boom and bash outside the hollow shells of airplanes:
"I will take care of you, one by one,
Or better yet, let you do it for me!"

Pirooz shakes his head, mystified:
"So many people love you, God, so much!
Will you ever show them that you love them back a little, too?"
Pirooz is awakened by a silence as big as the universe,
And he whispers to himself,
"I must wake up before I can never wake up!"

3   The Desert Dances

The sun rises, and the Sonora sleeps.
Every animal sleeps, every plant sleeps.
The bats, bugs, rodents and reptiles sleep.
Even the great saguaros Rumi and Hafez sleep.
After a long and blistering day
The sun yawns, rolls over, and falls asleep,
And the poets reawaken and resume counting stars.
Rumi soon realizes he is counting alone.
"Hafez Jaan—my dearest Hafez—what is wrong?
There isn't a cloud in the sky."
Confesses Hafez: "But there is a cloud in my heart, I fear,
A cloud named Pirooz."
Rumi's cactus head nods. "Yes, it is a miracle how he came to us,
To two saguaros who are not saguaros at all!
I'm glad he found us, glad we saved him from himself."
Hafez adds: "So am I, but I am also sad."
Without reaching out, Rumi pats Hafez on the back.
"But that was last night, and these stars are begging
To be counted tonight—so count with me, Hafez! Count!"

But Hafez does not count, cannot count.
"After longing for so long, I have been touched by life again,
From the saddened lips of Pirooz.
How surprising, how enrapturing, how intoxicating!
I dare to hope, Rumi Jaan, I dare to dream,
But I think God wants me to taste life again!"
Rumi, who first as a mortal man, and now as an immortal spirit,
Has striven to find his bliss in the paradise of serenity,

Feels impatience rising up his solid cactus stalk.
"But Pirooz sang a song of death, not life.
His mind was a ship with a torn sail,
His soul was whipped by wolfish waves of dissimulation,
His destination was the port of annihilation,
And the foreigner within him lashed him like the Caspian winds.
Did you hear how he struggled with the accents
In his voice, his feelings, his thoughts, and his resolve?
Thank God we need not struggle with so many accents.
Thank God you and I are dead!"
The sap running in Rumi's veins is suddenly sweet:
"Yet you are right, Hafez Jaan,
Though Pirooz in his distress could not tell a rose from a thorn,
He dardedeled with us, loved us, showed us great respect."

Hafez stares down at the empty sand,
Remembering the frail mortal who visited them the night before,
Remembering the frail mortal he once was himself,
Remembering exactly how he looked as a boy,
As a grown man, and as a man grown old, and now as a cactus.
He says to Rumi: "I don't blame Pirooz for not knowing
Who he is, where he is, or what he must do, or be.
I was once such a man myself,
And this old poem of mine is my proof:

Neither in life nor in death did I ever learn
Whence I came from, or where I am now.
I bemoan with pain and regret
That my own state is still unknown to me."

Rumi tries to lighten Hafez's heart with a joke:
"Just when I am getting used to you as a cactus,
You turn into a Pirooz!"
As Hafez laughs, his melancholy deepens:

36

"No, no, I am not a Pirooz.
For all my rebelliousness and all my spunk,
Pirooz is much braver with his life than I ever was.
He left his city for a new city—Tehran for New York.
He left his country for a new country—Iran for America—
And fought injustice whenever he could.
I, however, spent all of my seventy years in Shiraz,
Endlessly walking the same streets, drinking from the same wells.
Still, I felt like a foreigner in Shiraz, and suffered much in Shiraz,
But never found the courage to leave Shiraz, until death in Shiraz."

When Hafez falls silent Rumi sighs with gladness,
Thinking that his companion's sorrow is spent.
But as soon as he resumes counting, Hafez resumes his lament:
"I dissimulated, too, like Pirooz, so I know his pain.
Pirooz came to us, trusted us, opened his heart to us,
And welcomed us to all its chambers.
Now he needs us, even as prickly and dead as we are!
How can we refuse his invitation to save his life?"
Rumi wishes he had human feet, to pace away his frustration.
"We *did* save his life! Don't you remember?
He went away determined to try again,
His belly filled with my milk, your umbrella shading his eyes."
Hafez wishing he, too, could pace, reminds Rumi, that:
"We did not save him—we merely prolonged him!
Filling him, no doubt, with more doubts!"

Rumi suddenly feels top-heavy,
As if a nest of termites has nibbled away his rooty toes.
Finding nothing new to say, he relies on his own old adage:
"To rebuild an aging house, one must wreck the old edifice."
Then he shrugs the way trees shrug, and asks:
"Did we succeed in spoiling Pirooz's death wish?
As a first step to saving and revitalizing him?

Perhaps yes, perhaps no!
All we know for sure is that he is in God's hands."
"Rumi!" Hafez answers, almost in a scream,
"How can you say Pirooz is in God's hands,
When either by His direct designs
Or the indirect design of His universe,
God put Pirooz squarely in our hands?"
"Please," Rumi begs, "'In God's hands' is only an expression."
Hafez is suddenly serene: "Rumi Jaan, you spoke of doubts.
From this minute on I will defeat even doubts about doubts!
But there is more in my heart than just doubt,
For I am no longer resigned to never knowing
The secrets of Creation, as I was in the past."
Exasperated, Rumi scolds his friend:
"You wish to know the impossible secrets of Creation, Hafez?
It seems you have forgotten *my* poem:

What could the dead soil know about the sun, about the light?
How could the created know the creation?"

It is Hafez's turn to scold: "Remember, I am the one who remembers.
I do respect the old wisdoms, the old reasonings and answers.
But man faces new questions—so he must invent new answers!
Science is the way to truth now."

The fault line under Hafez has shifted.
Rumi is the one quivering now.
"You really are beginning to sound like Pirooz," he says.
Answers Hafez: "If I sound like Pirooz,
It is because I have touched the life in Pirooz.
And so my new life will have a new purpose.
I want to journey to where man has gone.
I want to journey to where Pirooz has gone.
To this new world I must be gone."

Rumi gasps: "You want to follow Pirooz to New York?"
"Yes, absolutely," Hafez shouts. "I want to go to New York!"
Says Rumi: "You are the mad Hafez,
My beloved Hafez, the everlastingly curious Hafez,
The conqueror of falsehood and hypocrisy Hafez,
The lover of freedom and truth Hafez.
Now you flick away caution as if it were a dead mosquito,
And thirst to gain the knowledge of this temporary world!
Why? Why?"
Hafez now looks deeply into Rumi,
As the bruised child looks deeply into his father, saying:
"I know it and I know it that Pirooz needs me in person.
Our old books may be of no help to him any more.
And, I confess, I need him in person, too, Rumi Jaan.
How much can I gain by reciting the Koran or my own *Divan* ,
Neither containing the knowledge of modern times?
Even in death I refuse to be bound by irrelevance
Or the glorified past!
I know it and I know it that I must go where life has journeyed,
Where science and art and faiths and law have journeyed,
While we stood still, our feet bound in sand and death.
I must go before I cannot go, and as Pirooz has said,
I must wake up before I can never wake up."

Rumi does not want Hafez to abandon him,
For he was abandoned once before by his beloved Shams,
The wandering mystic who wandered into his life in Konya,
The city where he taught and preached.
Shams had been searching for a perfect disciple,
And finding Rumi, knew that he had found him.
With Shams as his *pir*—his elder—and his guide,
Rumi became intoxicated with divine love.
He put aside his teaching and preaching,

39

Learning to write poetry, learning to sing,
Learning *sama*, the whirling dance, the Dervish dance.
He loved Shams. But then Shams disappeared.
And now Hafez wants to disappear.

Rumi wants to cry, as he cried for Shams.
But in death he has no tears.
So he says: "But I'll miss you, Hafez.
Omar Khayyam, the bat who nests in my chest, will miss you.
How sad, the bat gobbles nasty bugs,
Pollinates plants, that so nourish people, and
Yet the ignorant believe he, the bat, is a bad omen.
Imagine a great gift of God thought by many to be the enemy of man.
How tragic, how sad—ignorance is Hell for those who know."
Hafez smiles: "Yes, ignorance is Hell, I will say it again and again.
That is why I'm returning to life again,
To learn and to learn, again and again."

Hafez feels a palpitation in his saguaro stalk.
He knows God has bestowed upon him a heart,
Fulfilling his desire for a new life.
He also knows that Rumi is hurting from his decision.
So he spreads his cactus arms, as if welcoming a new idea.
"Rumi Jaan!" he says. "Why not come with me?
We will look after Pirooz together, learn of man's progress together,
Just as we counted the stars together."
Rumi shakes his head wildly. "I cannot go! And you should not go!
Meddling in the affairs of mortal men,
With more than the words in our books,
Is meddling with God's divine design."
Hafez loves Rumi and does not want to hurt him.
Yet he knows he must journey to modern times.
"But don't you see, God Himself is meddling!
He has just given me a jubilant heart, a heart agitated with desires.

Rumi Jaan, please, come with me to New York!
It is God's wish!"
Rumi remains as silent as
All the other cactuses in the desert combined.

Hafez sadly hangs his green head and to Rumi says:
"I will miss you, I already miss you.
I will miss, and I already miss, Khayyam the Bat,
I will miss, and I already miss, all our desert friends."
He now sees, for the first time ever,
Dew streaming down Rumi's face,
And wishes for human hands to brush the drops away.
"Remember, Mowlana, these words of your own:

If your house sits on a treasure,
You must wreck it before reaching the treasure.
But then, you must build a new house in its place,
Better than the one you had to wreck!"

Suddenly Hafez begins to dance and sing,
His legs still fixed in the sand but his arms
Moving in indescribable curves as if made of green rubber.
His lyrics fill the desert,
From the bottom of the sand to the top of the sky:

"Let us rise up and scatter flowers around,
And fill our cup with wine,
And tear and turn the world upside down,
And fashion a new order and a new life!
If one boasts of knowledge, or the other spews some nonsense,
Come and pitch their claims to the judgment of the ultimate judge.
If you desire heaven, then come to the tavern with us!
Then while intoxicated by love,
We will hurl you and bathe you in the Kosar,

The river that flows gently in heaven."

"Yes, my beloved Rumi," says Hafez, as he dances.
"The tavern I wish to visit now is called The Modern Times.
And the wine I wish to drink is the New Knowledge.
I want to know who this dear Pirooz really is,
Why he came to us, two prickly old cactuses,
And spoke to us with such love and admiration."
Now Hafez swings his arms, faster and faster and faster still,
As he repeats the mantra: "I want to know, there is no sin to know.
Know the self, know the other, and know the world, Hafez."

Suddenly Khayyam the Bat soars from his nest in Rumi's chest,
And holds wings with a silver-white dove,
The reincarnated soul of the great Sufi poet Attar,
Who sucks the nectar of the saguaros and yet pollinates the saguaros.
Heavenly pearls of rain begin to fall, fall, and fall,
Seducing the Cristate Saguaros to spread their fan-like crowns
And jump and dance, and dance and jump.
Acacia and wild asters and the furry Teddy-Bear Cholla,
Having longed for rain for such a long time, join the dance.
An ancient volcano spews a smoky dance.
The docile Gila monster and its neighbor, the industrious pack rat,
Spin like the Dervishes, spin and dance and dance.
The humble Creosote plants, covering every valley, laugh.
A hill leaps like a giant happy drunk frog.
The mountain lion roars and begins to dance.
The rattlesnakes rattle their joy and dance.
The centipedes kick in unison their fifty pairs of legs,
And dance like Radio City Music Hall Rockettes.
Pursued by its own dust and its own enthusiasm,
The roadrunner dashes to the horizon to tell all the party is on.

Hafez's resurrection, his joy of life,

His dancing and dancing and singing and singing,
And the giggling rain, giggling and raining,
Cleansing and bathing everything
For this magnificent birthday party thrown by God,
Transforms thousands of species, animals and plants alike,
Into a grand troupe of happy dancers.
They cry and laugh and celebrate a new life together.
And when Rumi turns to wish Hafez God's speed,
Hafez already is gone.

And God for once unknots His thick knotted brow
And smiles a dazzling purple tulip smile,
And feels an un-godly urge to join the dance.

4   Education Of The Beast

Ten stories above Riverside Drive,
In an apartment shared with too many books and roaches,
Professor Pirooz tries to shower away his morning doubts.
But the soap and hot water are useless,
And the day will have to begin, doubts or no doubts.
He makes tea and toast, but touches neither.
He chooses a beret from his tree of berets
And unlocks the door's seven locks.
He descends to the street and, head-down, heads
To the great temple of American aspiration
Called Columbia University, resting like a huge bowl of plaster fruit
Between hot, saucy Harlem and the cool leaves of Central Park.

Since returning from the desert Pirooz has tried so hard
To change his unchanging life,
To unstick himself from the mud of complacency,
From the mud of excuses, from the mud of despair.
He has changed from white bread to whole wheat,
And instead of drinking Sanka he now grinds his own beans.
And he has begun volunteering at an orphanage,
Reading funny stories to the children,
Children starved for a sliver of attention,
Children starved for a sliver of love and laughter.
He is even teaching some of them chess.

He has planted the seeds squeezed from a lemon.
And already they are sprouting in pots on his sill,
Reaching for the light outside

Just as their gardener, Pirooz, reaches for the light inside himself.
Yes, Pirooz has made so many changes since returning,
And yes, there will be so many more changes to come.
For one thing he is eager to find a new lover.
Maybe it will be the shy poetic brunette
Who sold him that yellow beret and Italian silk tie.
Pirooz has requested, and been granted,
A leave of absence for the upcoming term.
Already he is planning what to do with this gorgeous gift of time:
His plan is not to plan one single minute of this time!
His plan is to explore it and enjoy it,
Every serendipitous pleasure, every serendipitous trial.
Most of all, by not planning, he plans
To find that perfect poem hiding in his heart.
And when he finds it, and reads it,
He will be free at last from the prison called Profession.

He also has begun taking flying lessons,
To fulfill his boyhood dream to dance on the clouds.
His instructor is a woman, a former student of his,
Who threw away her books for the pleasures of the sky,
Who now lifts his spirit with or without a plane,
Who sits beside him, tempting his palpitating heart to soar
Higher and higher to both known and unknown places.
Already in just a few lessons he has noticed
That as she goads him to fly the little plane higher,
His own inner horizons are expanding,
And the irrelevant particulars of his grounded life
Are shrinking and shrinking, soon to nothing, he hopes.
He has noticed that as she commands him to descend,
To touch the runway, speed up and take off again,
That in his new life, he too, is doing much taking off.
To Pirooz, death now seems worlds away,
Books, lovers, flights, stories and poems away,

Beyond the horizons of horizons, the most awayest of aways.

Now his shoes take him between the Charles Keck statues
Of Letters and Scientia, to his classroom and his lectern.
When finally he lifts his eyes he no longer sees what
For too many years he used to see: rising rows of blank frog faces
Waiting to snap with sticky tongues the flies of truth that
Boiled from his dusty notes and tumbled from his dusty tongue.
Now he sees only ascending terraces of bright, eager frog faces.
"Where were we—if not everywhere?" he asks his students.
They laugh and he laughs and the class begins.

His day ticks away, each second lasting ten exciting seconds,
Each hour shrunken to one momentous minute.
Happy, full frogs hop away, eager, empty frogs hop in.
And all the time he is teaching, prancing about, flailing his arms,
He is also dreaming of seconds and minutes and hours yet to come.
At last it is three o'clock.
Pirooz, still busy in his day-dream world,
Hurries for the subway, for the No. 9 train south,
Which will worm-hole him through time and space,
Depositing him 100 blocks away in Greenwich Village,
Where he will drink too much espresso and play too much chess,
And perhaps debate something he knows little about,
With somebody he knows nothing about,
Until the afternoon and evening pass.
But as his foot dangles over the subway steps,
A voice vaguely familiar calls out from the rumbling street:
"Haleh shoma chetoreh, professor?" (How are you, professor?)
Pirooz withdraws his foot and twists,
Not noticing that the words are in Persian.
He squints at the smile inside the taxi revving at the curb.
It is a prodigious smile, a mystical smile,
Belonging to a man no older than twenty.

He is handsome, with dark eyes, mustache, and loose black hair.
"How about a cab today?" the young cabby asks.
"Why not?" Pirooz hears himself reply.
And so, seduced by a friendly face he has never seen before,
Pirooz trots to the cab and slides in.
"Greenwich Village?" asks the cabby.
"Yes, the Village," stammers Pirooz with surprise.
The cab jerks and jerks and jerks, and enters the flow.
Without waiting for Pirooz to recover from the quake of his surprise,
The cabby delivers an aftershock:
"How delightful to find you in good spirits, Pirooz!"
Pirooz is indeed shocked: "How is it you know my job and name?
Did I scribble them across my forehead, perhaps?
And forget all about it, as I do other things, perhaps?"
The cabby grins, saying, "Your forehead is perfectly clear.
It is your memory that's today unclear!"

The cab grovels beneath a red light and then growls away.
"What do you mean, unclear?" Pirooz asks.
The cabby is laughing now, enjoying his puzzled passenger:
"Only three weekends ago you asked me the very same question—
'How is it that I know your name?'"
"Impossible!" protests Pirooz. "Three weekends ago I was not here.
Three weekends ago I was —"
The cabby finishes for him, laughing as he talks:
"Lost in the Sonora talking to saguaros.
Pirooz! Don't you recognize me without my green skin and prickles?
I am Hafez! The poet! The star-counting cactus
Who magically grows umbrellas from his arms,
And now drives a taxi in New York!
Are you surprised I changed into a man, and came to visit you?"
Pirooz blinks at the happy eyes in the rearview mirror,
And, shaking his head, sighs: "Surprised and not surprised.
I had convinced myself that you and Rumi were real,

Then just this morning re-convinced myself it was a dream after all.
But now it is easy to believe everything:
If a poet can become a cactus, glued in the sands of a desert,
Then a cactus can become a man, glued to the seat of a taxi."
As Pirooz talks he searches the cab, as if looking for a lost ring.
"Where are you hiding, Rumi Jaan?
You are not the cab itself, are you, Rumi Jaan?"
The image of Rumi as a wheeled yellow ball makes Hafez chuckle.
"No, no, Pirooz! He is still a cactus counting stars,
Still thinking it unwise for me to follow you to New York.
But I had to follow you, to feel how you feel,
To see this marvelous future you live in!"
The cab turns down the avenue named for Columbus,
The discoverer of places already discovered.
"I missed you, Pirooz Jaan!" Hafez says.
"I have missed you all my life," Pirooz replies.
Then he mumbles to himself, *"Beh haghe harf-haye nashnofteh!"*
(I vow, the unbelievable has come true before my own eyes.)

"So," asks Hafez, as they stop and go, and stop and go,
"You teach at that school back there?"
It is Pirooz's turn to laugh: "I show up there,
And my students furiously fill their notebooks there—
But do I teach there? Not what I really want to teach."
Hafez is nodding his head. "I know what you mean.
My driving is not exactly driving, either.
I sometimes mistake the gas for the brake,
Or bump into bumpers or go the wrong way on one-way streets.
Yet my license insists I am a driver!"
They turn onto Broadway, just missing a jaywalking woman
Carrying a tiny white poodle in her huge purple purse.
"Dummy!" the poodle woman shouts.
Growls Hafez: "In Shiraz I was a smart man.
But in New York I am apparently not a smart man."

Pirooz sighs sympathetically, saying,
"Presidents proclaim that America is a celebration of difference.
But America demands conformity to the norm.
America ties individuals legally with ropes made of dollar bills . . . "
Hafez has heard a word he does not know.
"The norm? What is the norm?"
Answers Pirooz: "It is the pulp of your soul after the
Leviathan called Education has squeezed the exotic juices out of you."
Hafez is puzzled: "Education, a slithering monster from the deep?"
Pirooz sits silently, hands on his knees,
Watching the stuck traffic, listening to the shattering horns.
"Let me educate you about education in America, Hafez:
Our bodies are soaring toward the stars,
But our souls are nailed to the ground.
We search for extra-terrestrials curiously,
But refuse to look at ourselves critically.
Compared to what we could be, we remain so imperfect."
Protests Hafez: "Come on, Pirooz, all is not all that bad.
There is more freedom today, more wine, more books.
Even the norms you decry are not as bad as the norms of Ancientday!"

The cab crawls on through the noisy chaos,
Through the Sodom of Times Square and the Gomorrah of Chelsea.
"Go on," Hafez urges. "I didn't mean to silence you with my optimism."
Pirooz is angry and the hair under his beret is itching.
"And I didn't mean to depress you with my pessimism."
He lifts his beret and scratches, saying,
"I, too, want to believe that education can bring the best to man;
That we can remain curious like a child, and laugh like a child;
Grow toward perfection with every experience and every generation.
But here is the problem, my curious Hafez:
Who will decide what knowledge is best? Whose teaching is best?
Unfortunately, it is the powerful who dictate their truth best!

49

And although religious indoctrination is banned in schools,
They nevertheless indoctrinate a National Religion in schools.
In this religion created by slave owners ages ago
Columbus is the prophet and the Founding Fathers apostles.
The Constitution is the holy book.
The National Anthem is the hymn.
The flag, carried on shoulders like a cross,
Ruffles with stars and rivers of blood,
Each representing a chunk of captured real estate.
Hell is jail and heaven is success.
Money is god, so in money we trust.
We do not educate our children to become wise and creative.
We educate them to become functional, obedient, and employed."
Hafez shakes his head: "Nothing has changed in the soul of man.
Education has failed in the soul of man."

Pirooz is nearly in a frenzy now,
His arms flapping like the wings of a caged hen:
"But any proposal to change the system faces acrimonious debate,
Not about what is good for students, or society,
But what suits parents and politicians.
And since no one from outer space will help us,
Then who but us can save us from us and educate us?
Certainty not television—that foul mouth of falsehood
Of the money and for the money,
Inflicting that horrible addiction called consumption!"

They reach 34th Street and wait for shoppers and beggars
To flood across the beeping, beeping street.
Pirooz, exhausted by his lament,
Wishes that his beret were as large as a quilt,
So he could pull it over his head and disappear,
The way frightened children disappear under their blankets at night.

With his eyes he begs Hafez for permission
To end the re-experiencing of his own long agony.
But Hafez is insistent: "We still have some blocks to go, Pirooz Jaan.
Tell me why these patriot-preacher-teachers don't rebel?"
"We teachers may look like ghosts," Pirooz moans.
"But we are not ghosts—We have to eat."
"My heart breaks for you," Hafez says, "but are you really powerless?
In my day, teachers sat atop very high pillows."
Pirooz answers angrily: "Today teachers' pillows are very flat,
Flattened by the weight of regulations and laws.
We can't even stop our students from shooting each other.
That is how powerless we are!"

They reach Bleeker Street and Hafez pulls to the curb,
Knocking over a rack of free newspapers.
"Here you are, Pirooz Jaan, safe and sound."
Pirooz looks at Hafez's grin and digs into his pocket for his wad of bills.
Hafez waves his hands: "No no, Pirooz Jaan, this ride is on me."
Pirooz feels faint, a little foolish.
Does he just get out of the taxi now and go on about his business?
As if Hafez were just any other cabby?
As if this ride was just another dream to awaken from and forget?
Says Hafez: "Hurry up, Pirooz! Get out!
Those other drivers are honking their horns."
So Pirooz hops out and waves, not knowing
If he will ever see Hafez again.
He watches the cab disappear into the gas fumes and blaring horns.
Shaken, feeling lonely, he hurries toward The Sad Ghazal,
The coffee house with the wobbly green chairs
And the tiny cracked cups of strong espresso.
He takes only a few steps before he feels a hand on his shoulder.
It is Hafez, a grinning Hafez.
"I have decided to join you!" says Hafez.
Pirooz can see the numerous questions in his eyes.

5 Espresso & Consciousness

The Sad Ghazal is packed with the usual people,
Some animated, some in a trance as if posing for Rodin.
Some are sipping, some chattering, some lost in games of chess.
Some are reading, some are scribbling away at novels and poems.
Pirooz and Hafez sit at a table by the windows.
A waitress arrives and takes their order.
Pirooz does not know what to say to Hafez,
And Hafez is not interested in saying anything at all.
He is soaking in the people, inside the cafe and out there on the street.
They are of every color, from the whitest pink to the bluest black.
There are men holding hands with men,
Women holding hands with women,
There are dogs as small as rats pulling people as big as bears.
There are young faces furious that time moves too slow,
Old faces filled with fear because time moves too fast.
There are people who look rich, people who look very poor.
Languages as varied as the songs of birds in jungles,
Twist and twirl and intertwine unimaginable notes,
Creating exotic perfumes of sound.
"Quite a Babel," Hafez finally says.
The waitress brings their first espressos and they sip and sip and sip.
"Hafez," says Pirooz, "do you know that you
Are still the most popular poet in Iran?
That your *Divan* is more popular than the Holy Koran?
That it has been translated into languages
That did not even exist in your time?
That the great German poet Goethe loved it,
And like other poets was inspired by it?"

Hafez's entire body nods, slowly and sadly.
"I was the first Johann came to see when he died.
He praised me until I could take it no longer,
So I hid at the bottom of a lake as a clam until he went away.
I hope you are not going to praise me like that, Pirooz Jaan."

Emboldened by the espresso,
Pirooz reaches across the little table and takes the poet's hands.
"How can I not praise you, Hafez, when your poems
Are heavenly wine, becoming more intoxicating with time?
The great epic poet Ferdowsi revitalized Persian—
You beautified it into a bride.
You love Persian and Persian loves you.
What lovers you make—one making the other more enchanting."
Hafez pulls his hands away. "Pirooz, if you don't stop this nonsense
I will turn myself into a clam right here."
As Pirooz slides apprehensively down the back of his chair,
Hafez explodes with laughter and takes Pirooz's hands in his.
"Don't worry, I won't turn into a clam—that is worse than being a cactus!
I appreciate your good words, yet they seem so unlike you,
You, the one impressed not even with God!"
Says Pirooz shyly: "My compliments are from the heart, Hafez Jaan."

Two more cups of espresso arrive,
And so do two enormous bagels sprinkled with sesame seeds.
Hafez sips and chews and lets his frustration flow:
"In life I was condemned by a few and loved by some.
Now you tell me in death I am condemned by none and loved by many,
Even by those who cannot understand my Persian pen,
That publishers have become rich off my labors while I drive a taxi.
What kind of world is this modern world of yours?"
Pirooz answers him: "Hafez, you are like the world itself,
Full of enigmas unresolved.
Your life is an enigma, your love and lovers an enigma,

Your faith is an enigma and your *Divan* is an enigma,
A miracle of words with no claim it came from God.
So don't play humble with me, Hafez!
Surely you must know the secret of this universal love for you."
Hafez lets his mustache twist into a grin.
"You have answered your own question," he says.
"You said everything about me is enigmatic—and you are right!
What people don't understand they usually praise.
Ask God, who is understood least and praised most,
About awe and admiration!"
Pirooz dips his finger into the thick brown sugary drops,
Congealed like bitter honey at the bottom of his cup.
He sucks on his fingers and watches the way women
Give the handsome Hafez second, third, and fourth glances.
He says: "You rebelled against all that exists in heaven and on earth.
Remember, Hafez, your own poem:

Come, let us scatter flowers around and fill your cup with wine,
And tear, and turn the world upside-down . . . .

"You criticized creation, the rulers, the clergy,
The scholars, false Sufis, the rich crowd and the jealous crowd,
And then you bashed yourself for being just like them,
A dissimulating hypocrite concealing your beliefs out of fear,
And for being just as greedy for pleasures of the skin!"

Hafez erupts with another of his thunderlaughs, saying:
"I certainly was greedy, and certainly still am!
How can you stand living in this city, Pirooz?
So many alluring young women roaming around half naked,
As if in a bathhouse, heads, arms, and legs uncovered.
Even those parts covered press against their coverings
Like the flesh of a plum against its purpled skin."
Hafez looks about, worried that his voice is as loud as his lust.

No one is listening or watching but he whispers just the same.
"I remember this poem I wrote about myself:

Bring wine, and let us be intoxicated
Since if you look soberly, you will see,
That the learned, the men of God,
The rulers, and even Hafez,
Engage in hypocrisy and dissimulation."

When Pirooz adds that, "Even God dissimulates,"
Hafez is provoked: "Even God?"
"Yes," Pirooz says. "He refuses to tell us the origin of consciousness,
To tell us how the seen brain creates, or couples with, the unseen mind,
How biology and electromagnetism ascend to belief
In His existence and His goodness,
If the self, the soul, and spirit are just fancy words
For a bunch of programmed neurons?"

"What is your secret?" Pirooz asks Hafez,
As they walk toward Washington Square.
"Your poems are layered with so many ideas and meanings.
They reveal so much yet seem to reveal so little."
Hafez, eyes fixed on a man dressed in leather and chains,
Walking a frilly monkey not much bigger than a doll,
Nervously straightens his mustache and replies:
"Some of the ambiguity in my poems is there playfully,
Some incidentally, some intentionally,
Layers and layers of disgusting disguise,
To protect me from powerful authorities and angry crowds.
So most of what was in my heart remained in my heart.
But I don't have to tell you about dissimulation, Pirooz, do I?
You do complain about it as if it were a disease of the soul.
And of course dissimulation is a disease of the soul,

55

Tragically inflicted on man by man, like so many other diseases."
Pirooz takes a final sip of his thick, cold espresso.
"Yes, Hafez Jaan. The most important and interesting truths
Always remain unsaid."
"How do you know what you say is true?" Hafez demands.
Says Pirooz with a smile, "If I state the *uncontradictable*—
Which surely I try to do—
Then I've got the truth as shiny as sunlight
Captured on the brim of a great big hat!"

As they cross the street and enter the park,
Pirooz puts his hand on Hafez's shoulder, saying:
"Now it is I who remembers one of your own poems:

With whom or for whom can you open your heart,
If you are the nightingale that must remain still as death
Even when the roses bloom."

They find a bench surrounded by pigeons and squirrels,
And people with wheels on their feet.
"Thank you for remembering my poem," Hafez says.
Pirooz takes off his beret so the evening breeze can
Gently blow his dark brown hair, and answers:
"The Koran was in your heart, Hafez Jaan,
But your *Divan* is in many hearts."
As they talk, one of the people with wheels on their feet slices by,
Just inches from their toes.
"Who are these people?" Hafez grumbles.
"Rollerbladers," Pirooz responds,
"A race of creatures impatient with the speed of evolution."
They laugh and then laugh at their laughter.
"Why do you have to dissimulate, Pirooz?" asks Hafez,
"Everything in this New York of yours seems so free and easy."
Answers Pirooz: "That is the enigma of America.

We praise freedom and rejoice in it, as if it were morning prayer.
But when you try to live it, reality rips you in two.
Your body is left free but your spirit is put in jail."
"Have you experienced this yourself, Pirooz?"
Pirooz throws his arms over his head and groans,
"I am marginalized not only by my colleagues,
But even by some of my students, who,
Thinking that I am a bowl of acid, keep their distance
Lest I spill my freedom on them,
And burn holes in their expensive dreams."

The sky turns gray and it begins to sprinkle.
They walk west toward a coffee house called The Peacock,
Where the espresso, Pirooz promises, is very good.
"Tell me," Pirooz asks as the drops tickle their ears,
"What is or who is Rumi's God?"
Says Hafez: "Rumi is not here to defend or define his beliefs,
But whichever way he faces, he sees the beautiful face of God.
Not the God everyone knows, but the God no one knows."
Pirooz understands, asking,
"And you, Hafez Jaan? Just what are your beliefs?"
The poet grows thoughtful, saying:
"I know Abraham and all the prophets.
I know Erfan, the Sufi knowledge of the self and the soul.
I know all the philosophies and metaphysics of my time.
I even know some astronomy and physics.
I have studied Pantheism, Mitraism, et cetera, et cetera.
But I am a *Rend*—I understand them all
But I am not convinced by any unconditionally!"

They pass shops selling flowers and shops selling fruit,
Shops selling wine and shops selling bread,
Selling sunglasses, hats, black shiny underwear and shoes,

Everything but conscientiousness or consciousness.
"We must start a new religion," says Pirooz,
As they duck into The Peacock. "We will call it *Rendism*.
It will be a congregation that strives to know more and more,
So it can believe less and less, thus understanding more and more.
Transcendence through skepticism!
Our prophet will be Truth! Our heaven Liberty!
Our prayer will be a single word—justice!
And our God will be Love!"
Hafez joyfully claps his hands as if at a play, saying,
"Yes! Yes! our God will be Love,
The most perfect Trinity whether blasphemous or not!
First, carnal love, the skin-deep love for a beautiful mate.
Second, the ideal and unattainable love,
Which combines the beauty of appearances
With the hidden beauty of the mind and soul.
Third, and highest, love for creation and for the creator,
Who makes possible all other loves and all other lovers."

They sit in The Peacock for hours,
Drinking double espressos as if they were goblets of wine,
Talking about the magical city pressing around them,
The tall buildings, the screaming sirens and screaming lights,
The silent screams of the lonely and abandoned.
They talk about the people and the way they rush about
To make money and more money for the corporate deities
Sitting in the highest offices atop the highest towers.
They talk about the city's incredible energy, its frantic inertia,
A city in constant motion without ever moving,
A hive full of bees, a hill full of ants, a school of minnows
Fighting to survive in a shrinking puddle.
Pirooz laments: "Had I known about the tardigrade
Before I was conceived and born, I would have asked God
To make me one of those microscopic beings."

Hafez, as jumpy with caffeine as Pirooz, asks,
"Tardigrade *digeh chee-yeh?*" (What, pray tell, is a tardigrade?)
Pirooz, his fast words tripping over his quivering lips, explains:
"Tardigrades are microscopic invertebrates with ambling gaits.
Called water bears—the invisible sort—they live roly-poly lives
Among the algae in sweet lakes and bitter seas.
They can be zapped with the worst and yet laugh and survive:
Chilled to degrees cold even to Antarctica, boiled to scorching heats,
Put in a vacuum with nothing to eat,
Smashed by immense hydrostatics as powerful as cannon balls blasting,
Tardigrades survive it all, as if joy-riding on a carousel."
Hafez, brows arched high, observes, "They are very tough little bugs!"

Pirooz's head is bobbing like the head of a poppy in the wind.
"The tardigrade is a cunning genius who shrinks himself
To a suspended animation when in danger,
Then blows himself up once the trouble is gone,
To resume life gracefully as if no harm was intended and no harm done."
Pirooz now thumps on the table with his fist,
As question after question swarms in his mind.
"Where is our genius and astuteness, that creative consciousness
That turned us from monkeys into men?
Why are we creating a world where only the tardigrade can survive?"
Asks Hafez: "What is this consciousness you speak of so often?"
Pirooz calms himself and answers: "What is consciousness?
Your question does not surprise me, Hafez Jaan,
For while consciousness is as nosy as a cat's nose
When it comes to minding the business of others,
It remains quite quiet about its own mind.
But for you, dearest Hafez, I will give your question a try:
Consciousness is awareness of the inner self and the outer self.
One can be more conscious or less conscious.
The attributes of consciousness
Are remembering, feeling, knowing, reasoning, choosing, and creating.

Self-consciously humans expand their consciousness—
This is H-consciousness.
Monkeys fight, flee, feed, frolic, use tools
And arrange their social order—they have M-consciousness.
Computers drink electricity, reason and remember, and continually
Seduce humans to make them better—they have C-consciousness.
Trees long ago solved the mystery of flight with pollen and seeds,
And seem to get along happily without propellors or wings—
They fall asleep in the fall, then wake up in spring—
To support by photosynthesis the consciousness of all living things.
They have T-consciousness.
Stones have history but no memory, they are present but passive—
Thus they have NO-consciousness."
Hafez has enjoyed the professor's short lecture:
"It was nice of you to put humans first and monkeys second."
Answers Pirooz: "Perhaps that is just my own human bias,
Or perhaps we truly deserve top billing.
What is true, and sad, is that human consciousness
Too often is contaminated with confusions and falsehoods,
While monkeys seem free of these self-inflicted maladies.
But man can alter *human nature* and consciousness consciously.
And most amazing, Hafez Jaan,
Nature is more imaginative than consciousness,
Since things discovered are things never imagined."
"Hoo!" gasps Hafez, "I never thought that
Such a dark subject could be illuminated so white!"
Pirooz's head is shaking back and forth.
"Consciousness is rarely white, Hafez Jaan.
It is mostly gray, the color of the brain—
Which performs many tasks behind our conscious backs.
The truth is, our consciousness is forever slacking off,
So that our subconscious, by default, steps forward and rules.
And so, one is forever caught wondering:
'What on earth have I just done?'

Or 'Did *I* really do this?'
As bad as these lapses are for us as individuals,
They are multiplied six billion fold each day.
So the collective subconscious spoils
While our collective consciousness sleeps!"
Hafez is nodding his head: "The subconscious is a nuisance, all right.
You would think we could control it better!"
Answers Pirooz: "Unfortunately our brains are at its mercy.
Mother Nature wires our synapses for safety and sex,
Then the world enters our brain surreptitiously at birth,
And wielding carrots and sticks,
It stuffs and wires other synapses with even more sub-consciousness,
Without a word of explanation as to what, how, and why.
And unless one becomes aware of these secret stuffs,
One remains a programmed machine of nature,
Of a given time and place."

"Do you have a place to stay?" Pirooz asks as Hafez drives him home.
"I have only one bed, but you are welcome to it."
And so the two Persians, the poet and the professor,
Sleepy, but too full of espresso to sleep,
Ride the elevator to Pirooz's apartment,
Ten stories above the still vibrating street.
Pirooz shows Hafez the bed, and then,
Taking a pillow and a blanket, curls up on the sofa
And listens to the rapid thumping of his intoxicated heart.
"Hafez Jaan!" he calls out. "I'm so glad you came to New York!"
Answers Hafez: "One lost soul looking out for another, Pirooz Jaan."

6 Faal

The taxi dispatcher doesn't know that this Hafez is *the* Hafez,
The living ghost Hafez, the legendary poet Hafez.
The dispatcher only knows that this Hafez
Is an eager immigrant with the rudimentary ability
To grip a steering wheel and stomp a brake,
And reach his hand over the backseat for a fare.
Yes, to the dispatcher this Hafez is just a cabby, in a city of cabbies,
Pinballs to slap from street to street, bell to bell,
Collecting fares, fares, and more fares.
Yet, this Hafez loves being dispatched,
Loves the search for named and numbered streets,
To help weary people make their way.
His taxi is but a poem, a vehicle for transporting souls.
And so every morning after Pirooz leaves for his classroom,
Hafez hurries to his classroom, the street,
And helps his students, his passengers, find their way.

This afternoon the dispatcher sends Hafez
To a private high school with high iron walls,
To deliver a girl to her high-rise home,
In a high-rent neighborhood on the high east side.
Hafez is running late, which is no surprise.
Everyone is rushing in New York, feeling late in New York,
Even as they glance at their watches like head-bobbing sparrows,
Looking up, checking for dangers, before spearing another seed.
Hafez finds the school and bumps into the curb,
Dazzled as he spots his fare—the most beautiful of girls,
The freest of spirits caged in a school uniform.

He honks and honks his horn.

With her backpack stuffed full and more books in her arms,
She rushes toward his cab as if captured by the North Star.
The curious autumn wind scatters her curly black hair as she runs,
And lifts her pleated school-girl skirt like an umbrella opening up,
Revealing her tapered thighs and the scarlet panties hugging her hips.
As she runs and pushes at her skirt, the books tumble from her arms.
And what her panties cover screams to Hafez: "I am the will of God.
Even the wind revealing me is the will of God."

Hafez jumps from the taxi to help her gather her books.
She is already on her knees—oh, what knees—when he drops to his.
People, sparrowing their watches, rush around them indifferently,
Anxious not to miss their appointments.
"Let me help you," Hafez manages to say.
"Thank you," she says shyly, the music of her voice dovetailing
With her words into a song only God could have composed.
As they exchange the last book, the tips of their fingers touch.
Hafez feels that he is melting, a slow and sensuous melt,
That candles melt when the maidens of Shiraz read from his *Divan*.
Suddenly he is shocked, deep to the roots of his neurons.
The book passing between them *is* his *Divan!*

(Those touching fingers: his aflame, hers trembling.
Who knows why or how?
It may be fear, it may be joy, it may be both.
Those touching eyes: his bittersweet chocolate,
Hers the turquoise of the bluest sea,
Hugging and then kissing and then making love,
By the ethics of DNA, or the god of Synchronicity,
Or the god of unbelievable stories and happenings.)

Hafez opens the cab door for the girl, and when she is inside,

Closes it gently, as if tucking her in a blanket.
"You have my address?" she asks when he is behind the wheel.
Hafez turns, and seeing his face floating in her eyes, replies,
"Yes, yes, yes, yes—"

(Why is it that the great master of words
Can say no more than yes and yes and yes and yes?
Why is it that the angels of love flip and flop with joy
And rejoice with the music of his yes and yes and yes?
And why is it that the stars join hands and dance and celebrate?
Why is it he can only answer yes and yes and yes and yes?)

Hafez finds the right gear and the taxi plunges forward,
As though propelled by the sound of horns,
Protesting its vigorous advance into the grinding traffic.
His eyes spend more time in the mirror than on the street.
And seeing his *Divan* resting on her unreal lap,
Hafez is reminded of the ode that once dripped from the tip of his pen:

The fragrance of your curly hair will keep me intoxicated forever.
Your magical eyes put me in a trance,
Ruining me in the mystery of their lust!
The wind and I are both hopelessly lost: I in your luscious eyes,
And the wind in pursuit of your fragrant hair, running from its reach!

Somehow he remembers her address and somehow he finds it.
She smiles at him all the way to the revolving door
That envelopes her and spins her out of sight.

The next day Hafez does not wait for the dispatcher to dispatch him—
He dispatches himself and waits until the girl emerges from school.
Overnight she has grown even more beautiful.
Again his *Divan* is among her books.

64

Again when she asks him if he knows the address,
He answers yes and yes and yes and yes and so it goes day after day,
Each day the cabby and the schoolgirl
Finding a way for their fingers to touch and their eyes to make love,
Letting their silence say what they dare not say.
Then on the fifth day, when the girl slides into the taxi, she says,
"Take me to Central Park."
Her demand takes Hafez by surprise. "Not home?"
She smiles at his widening eyes,
At the handsome face with the great mustache.
"It's too nice a day to go home," she says.
Hafez protests: "But aren't your parents expecting you?"
Answers the girl: "The only things expecting me are the TV
And the leftovers in the refrigerator."

Hafez has only been in this modern city for a week,
Yet he has been watching TV and knows what she means.
Still, her request frightens him:
"I don't want to get you in trouble—or for that matter me!"
The girl leans forward and in a whisper says,
"Take me to Central Park, and join me.
I wish to read to you from the *Divan* of Hafez, the nightingale of Persia.
I want you to know Hafez as I do."
Hafez knows he should decline her invitation:
It is one thing for a spirit to save a dispirited professor,
And quite another for a spirit to fall in love with a spirited girl.
But her little hide-and-seek smiles are so full of expectation,
And her perfect skin radiates a serendipitous light,
Tightly engulfing her body like the finest silk.
"Yes I will join you," he says.
"I like poetry surrounded by the fall's falling leaves,
Dancing their Dervish dance while I'm ascending!"

Soon they are sitting on a bench by a pond filled with quacking ducks.

65

Perhaps they are quacking one of Hafez's songs:

In the morning the bird of the garden
Greeted a new flower: "Don't be so coy and flirting,
In this garden where many blossoms blossom just like you!"
The flower laughed and replied: "The truth hurts me not,
But no lover ever spoke so harshly to the beloved!"

Hafez feels the girl's hand over his and hears her giggle.
"Wake up—where are you?" she asks.
"High in the sky," he answers. "Waiting for you to bring me down."
Then he smiles as shyly as she is smiling.
"But tell me, first, what is your name?"
"My name is Mitra."
"Like me, you are a Persian?"
"Sort of—my mother was a Peace Corps volunteer.
On a ski slope near Tehran she met my father, a Persian,
With his backside on the slippery ground!
She helped him up, the way you helped me with my books.
They are divorced now.
And I live with my mother, a very busy corporate climber,
In this very greasy town to climb,
While my father is busy teaching physics three thousand miles away."
Mitra smiles sweetly until her loneliness has passed, then asks:
"How did you guess I was Persian? I have no accent whatsoever."
Says Hafez: "Your name is your accent, taken from the myth of Mitra,
The old Persian god of goodness and light.
Mitra captured and killed the sacred bull,
From whose blood all earthly life sprang.
Did you know that the Romans came within an inch
Of adopting Mitraism as the official religion
Of their empire, instead of Christianity?
Tell me, Mitra, are you a goddess in disguise?"

66

She smiles sardonically. "My mother says I act like a goddess,
But she is not giving me a compliment—now tell me your name."
"Hafez," answers Hafez,
She squints skeptically. "Hafez? Are you teasing me?"
"No! My name is really Hafez,
As much as the poet Hafez's name is really Hafez.
"*Beh haghe harf-haye nashnofteh!*" she says.
(I vow, the unbelievable has come true before my own eyes.)
Hafez is delighted: "You speak Persian!"
"My parents spoke Persian at home," she says with a shrug,
"And I was taught to read and write it when I was only four."
Hafez is astonished: "At four? You are a prodigy."
"No," she says, "I'm just a girl with smart parents—
Smart in everything but their love for each other."
The girl's maturity impresses Hafez,
As much as the body inside her uniform impresses him.
"Just how old are you, Mitra?"
She is defiant: "What does my age have to do with our reading poems?"
Hafez raises her hand and kisses it gently. "Sorry—
Even if you were a baby we would read them,
Even if I was six hundred years old."
As he says this his eyes fight not to notice
Her sweet-pear breasts as they press against her cotton blouse.
"If I were a baby? I will graduate this spring—with all A's—
And enter Columbia next fall on a full scholarship.
And I can play the harp, and I study ballet,
With a woman who once was the toast of St. Petersburg."

Hafez tilts his head playfully. "Mitra! How old are you?"
"Okay," she hisses, pretending to be angry, "I'm fourteen—
Which is the same age the great Hafez wished his lovers to be!"
Hafez trembles inside. "How do you know that?"
She taps the *Divan* on her knees, as if she was tapping Hafez's heart.

Mitra's words, Mitra's voice, Mitra's spring scent,
Mitra's supple lips, Mitra's knowing eyes,
Mitra's audacious and curious spirit,
Ignite an ancient smoldering in Hafez.
"You, you, you . . ." he stammers,
As if trapped between the cliffs of happiness and uncertainty.
"You, what?" she wonders, her heart drumming the rages of love.
Hafez catches the last of his breath,
Before his lungs collapse and his head explodes.
"Read, Mitra! Read!" he pleads.
Cool and triumphant, she demands answers from him:
"Aren't you going to tell me anything about you?
How old you are? Whether you like your work?"
Hafez can barely speak: "I am old enough
To have a taxi driver's license. Now read! Please!"

So Mitra opens the *Divan* , and says:
"I will read you the first lines in Hafez's book,
Though it is doubtful they are the first words he composed:

Arise wine-bearer, oh rise and swing that cup of wine to me.
Love seems easy at first, then come the difficulties!"

Hafez looks at the pages, spread sensuously like the petals of a rose.
Mitra is speaking in English,
But the words written on the page are in Persian.
Mitra continues to read:

"With the hope that the breeze will unveil her lovely face, and
Untie the knots in her hair, freeing her perfumed curls
Whose absence has been the cause of so much grief.
Tint your prayer rug with the forbidden wine
If the wise old Magi tells you so,
Since the truth-seeker knows well the pilgrim's rule of etiquette!

How can I have the time of my life,
Enthralled in the bosom of my beloved,
If bells scream incessantly: 'Bind your belongings to depart!'
With the black night storming and the wolfish waves frightening,
And the eddying whirlpools devouring,
How could the light-hearted on the shore
Know our imperiled fate at sea?"

Mitra stops reading and, drinking in the cabby's face, says:
"Hafez Jaan, let us take a Hafez faal."
The word *Jaan*, meaning my life, my soul, my beloved, sets Hafez on fire.
But those other words puzzle him: "What is a Hafez faal, Mitra Jaan?"
His puzzlement puzzles her: "You don't know what a Hafez faal is?
Even though your name is Hafez?"
Hafez cannot tell her that he's been dead for centuries,
Disguised as a cactus for some of them.
He can only shrug and say, "I know not what I know not,
Nor do I know why I know not.
I know that faal is fortune telling, but I know not about Hafez' *faal*."

Mitra shakes the dizziness from her head.
"Okay, Hafez, enough of the know-not stuff! A Hafez faal is this:
If you wish to know the future or make a difficult decision,
You refer to the *Divan* for help, saying:
'Hafez-e Shirazi, you know every secret,
I swear you to your *Divan* to tell me what I must know.'
Then you randomly open the book, and flip to the preceding page,
And read the ode you find there."
"You do?" asks Hafez, astonished by this strange use of his poems.
(How could I predict the future of others, he thinks,
When my own future was such a blur?)
Mitra nods. "For centuries kings have made war and peace by faal.
Marriages have been arranged by faal.
Journeys, cures, even business decisions have been made by faal.

Even today many people believe
That the *Divan* predicts and guides well."

Hafez is filled with wonder, and embarrassment, saying,
"I cannot believe that Hafez is so revered, and so trusted,
Especially about things he surely never meant to be entrusted with!"
Mitra is playful: "And how do you know that?"
Hafez answers quickly: "Just guessing, Mitra Jaan."
As they both giggle, Mitra opens the *Divan*,
And flips the page, and then puts the book
Into Hafez's outstretched hands.
"Read my faal for me," she says.
Hafez glances at the first line of the ode,
And then gently closes the book.
"That was my faal!" Mitra protests. "You lost it!"
"No, I did not," Hafez says.
He points to his heart and recites:

"The lonely days and nights when my lover was gone are gone,
And my faal shined bright, since Sirius was placed right,
And everything turned into a delight.
And the flirting, and the showing off of autumn,
Finally ended with the first zephyr of spring—thanks be to God."

"Watch out for the kite!" Mitra squeals.
Before she can finish her warning,
A huge green kite crashes at Hafez's feet.
He takes a long breath to replenish his startled lungs,
Then picks up the kite and with his eyes
Follows its long wriggle of yellow yarn
To a smiling Puerto Rican boy standing far away on a grassy hillock.

7 Ask Me Not About Love

Professor Pirooz finishes his last class
And walks to his apartment, happy that a long day is over,
Hoping that Hafez is just as tired as he is,
And won't want to talk all night about the mysteries of the modern world.

The elevator deposits Pirooz at his door,
And the key in his hand commands it to open.
He sees Hafez sitting cross-legged on the kitchen table
Eating a half-moon of melon while reading a book.
Inside he finds a Puerto Rican boy curled on his sofa,
Tattered kite resting in his baggy-jeans lap,
Dog droppings stuck on the bottom of his shoes.
Hafez welcomes him home: "Look who I found flying a kite!"
Pirooz, of course, does not recognize the boy.
On the streets of New York there are thousands of such boys
With cappuccino skin and Caribbean smiles.
Says Pirooz with a scowl: "I don't care who he is,
Just as long as he takes his dirty shoes off my couch."
Hafez throws open his arms: "It is our Rumi, Pirooz!
Here to look after me just as I came to look after you!"
Pirooz is surprised and not surprised—
After all, if Rumi can be a green cactus why not a brown boy?
He also is embarrassed by his inhospitable demand.
"Welcome to my humble home, Mowlana," he says.
"And please, if you wish, keep your shoes where they are."
Rumi laughs and turns himself into a man
With white beard, sharp eyes, and immaculate soles.

Pirooz had hoped to spend a quiet evening listening to music,
Reading somebody's novel, yawning himself to a peaceful sleep.
But now with both Rumi and Hafez in his apartment,
He is excited and awake: "So you were flying a kite, Mowlana?"
Hafez eagerly answers for Rumi: "He is a sneak, isn't he?
Spying on me with my new love!"
"I was not spying," Rumi insists,
"Merely enjoying *my* self while you were enjoying *your* self."
Hafez laughs at this and bites into another slice of melon.
"Once in heaven," he tells Pirooz,
"I found our dear master watching a pool of bathing virgins.
'They are beautiful, aren't they?' I said.
And he answered, with the straightest of faces,
'I was worried that one of them may drown.'
So I guess Rumi was watching me in the park because
He was afraid that *I* might drown.
Well, you showed up too late, Rumi Jaan—I have already drowned!
Drowned in new love by my new love, my perfect Mitra!"

Hafez recounts how fate put Mitra in his taxi,
Leaving out not a word, look or heartbeat between them,
Then suddenly he begins to sing:
"When I saw her tempting curls I felt my heart curling, too!
Yes, I am in love again, my love curling and curling, too!"
As he sings he leaps higher than Barishnykov,
More graceful than a nightingale just freed into spring,
Landing in front of the bewildered eyes of Rumi and Pirooz.
"Rumi Jaan, Pirooz Jaan," he pleads,
"Rejoice for me and rejoice with me,
And praise what is most worthy of praise—love!
My midnight dream ode is now a daylight reality!"
Pirooz is tingling. "Hafez Jaan," he cries,
"I know this ode of yours by heart.
But please recite it for me, so that I, too, can realize a dream."

Hafez is filled with love and appreciation.
"Yes! Of course I will recite it for you!
And for Rumi and for me!
I will even recite it for God, to remind Him
That the wishes of others are expecting His attention."
And so Hafez recites, his unworldly voice filling the apartment:

"Her lips dewy and her curls tangled, drunk, giggling and singing,
Her blouse half open—holding a jug of wine,
Her narcissus eyes sparkling and her lips alluring,
She slipped into my bed last night at midnight,
And brought her lips to my ear and whispered soulfully:
'Are you awake my aggrieved old lover?'
A lover who is tendered such a midnight drink
Believes not in love if he does not worship wine.
So ask me not if the wine was from heaven or earth,
Intoxicating or not.
I drank what she poured into my cup, since
The grinning wine and her tempting curls would seduce anyone,
And Hafez, too, to break his vows of repentance."

When Hafez is finished, Rumi and Pirooz run to him,
And the three hug and become one.

To celebrate the ancient poet's new love
Jiggling bottles of wine surface on Pirooz's coffee table,
As if out of nowhere.
The three Persians drink glass after glass,
Drowning themselves in the New World and the New Times.
Pirooz goes to the corner and rescues his *tar*,
Blowing years of dust off its two bowls and six starved strings.
He holds it in his arms like a baby and begins to strum,
Breaking his vows to his father never to play for anyone

73

Except for himself or his family,
For fear of being considered an *entertainer*,
Then a thing of disgrace in his family.
But tonight everyone is his family.
Even these two ghosts are his family.
Was he not a student of Hafez and Rumi?
Was he not saved from death by Hafez and Rumi?
Pirooz plays and sings, exhorting:
"Let the angels of dance dance
And let the angels of music make music.
Dance Hafez, dance and dance and dance.
Dance for Rumi, dance for Mitra and for me.
Dance for all Persians in diaspora,
Dance for all history in diaspora."

Hafez does begin to dance, clapping his hands over his head
The way macho flamenco dancers do.
Pirooz, filled with smiles, continues his song:
"Dance and dance and dance, Hafez,
And let the fires of love,
Ignited by truth, forgiveness, and happiness,
Induce everyone and everything to dance.
Let the world know that a new love is born
From the withered womb of the past and
The supple womb of the future.
Ashes to ashes, cactus to man,
A new man reinvigorated by new love!
Praise be to the new love of Hafez and Mitra!"

Now Rumi is dancing, too, and Pirooz is still plucking,
So furiously that the instrument seems to cry out:
"I'm in love, too! I'm burning and I'm hurting, too!
Hold me and play with me and let me dardedel with you!"

Rumi hears the tar's plea and begins to sing:

"Love is a sea with no shores, domed by a bubble of foam for sky.
Without love every motion dies and the wheel of heaven stops,
And existence becomes inanimate . . .
Life begets love and love begets life.
It is love that transforms the inorganic to plant,
And lures the plants to sacrifice themselves,
To be gifted with the spirit of a man!"

"Tell us more about love," the tar begs.
And Rumi obliges:

"When a man and a woman unite into one,
Together a new being they become.
And this I and this Us are made up to quench
The false thirst from self-adoration.
Or else, all the pronouns—I, you, we and them—
Become submerged in God, the beloved of all true lovers."

Now everyone has stopped dancing, and Pirooz has stopped playing.
"I am a modern man," says Pirooz,
"Who needs data and datum, bits and bytes of information.
Tell me more about this Mitra of yours, Hafez,
So I can feel the love in your heart inside my heart!"

Hafez clutches his breast and bubbles one of his famous odes:

"Ask me not, my beloved, how I've endured the pains of love.
Ask me not how I've swallowed your absence—the bitterest bane.
Ask me not.
"Throughout the world I've journeyed,
And at the end I've found a lover so dazzling
That I can't tell how, that I can't tell why.

Ask me not how the tears pour down from my longing eyes,
As I dream, reaching for her presence.
Ask me not why.
"With my own ears I heard last night her words,
So magic that I beg you to ask me not what they were.
Ask me not what.
"Why do you gaze at me and bite your lips to silence me?
I've tasted such ruby lips, but ask me not how sweet.
Without her in my humble nest I've suffered such heartaches
That I can't tell what or how, for it is so painful to recount.
Ask me not how.
"Although I've been lost in the path of love,
Yet with love I've ascended to such peaks that I can't tell how high.
Ask me not how high."

Pirooz, impatient for facts, tries to coax Hafez from his ambiguity:
"True, Mitra is magnificent beyond description,
But tell us something tangible, for instance, what does she do?"
Hafez, so filled with his love that he sees no reason to answer,
Nevertheless answers: "She is a schoolgirl."
Pirooz feels suddenly dizzy, as if suddenly hit over the head with
The twin hammers of dread and disaster.
"A schoolgirl, Hafez? How old did you say she is?"
Hafez beams: "Fourteen—the ideal age!"
Pirooz covers his mouth and sucks air through his fingers,
Grunting, "My God! My God! My God!"

Hafez ignores Pirooz's worried face
And continues his praise for the girl he loves:
"And she is so smart, Pirooz Jaan, so mature!
The school has jumped her ahead three years.
She will graduate next spring, and
Enter the same university where you teach,
Every penny of her tuition paid in full by her uncanny genius."

"My God, my God, my God," mumbles Pirooz again.

Rumi is perplexed by Pirooz's reaction: "Professor, What is wrong?"

Answers Pirooz: "Fourteen is a forbidden age in America.

She is just a teenager, and a young teenager at that.

Messing with a teenage girl is a fast ticket to hell,

Even for a man who pretends to be as young as you, Hafez!"

"What hell can there be for loving a young woman?" Rumi asks.

"The hell of jail," answers Pirooz. "For this is a different time,

With different beliefs and different laws.

The ready woman of your day is the radioactive child of ours."

Hafez, angry and astonished, breaks his silence:

"God proclaims by creation, my ears hear it and my eyes see it,

That Mitra is grown and ready to be a wife and a mother.

And no prophet or holy book forbids her,

And nature compels her to love and be loved.

Why, Pirooz, are so many things so unnatural in this modern world?

So much more rigid and ridiculous than in the ancient world?"

Answers Pirooz glumly:

"Remember that once your ancient world was the modern world,

And the ancient rules enlightened rules.

Times change but little changes.

Islam, Judaism, Christianity, the old religions of personal salvation,

Have been shoved aside by national religions.

Even here in America, as free as any land, people are made

To march uphill with their pockets filled with rocks of repression."

"Tell us more about this national religion," Hafez demands,

So we'll know if we are still permitted to breathe."

Pirooz throws up his hands. "For what use?

I have been preaching about the national religion for years.

My American students regurgitate it back to me on tests,

And then crawl off to their star-spangled prayer rugs

As if having heard or learned nothing,

77

As if I were a gull squawking in a hurricane!"
Rumi chuckles: "We are all gulls squawking in hurricanes,
So go ahead, preach to us—we will listen to every word with care."

And so Pirooz begins: "America's national religion proclaims that
Columbus discovered the Promised Land,
Which, mind you, was already promised and already discovered
By others who had lived here for thousands of years,
Thinking it was theirs.
This Columbus murdered the *Indians* he found
And confiscated their possessions and their lands,
And collected their souls and gave them to Abraham's God.
And then there was George Washington,
And his apostles, the Founding Fathers,
Who established the national religion,
With the Constitution as its scripture,
The Star-Spangled Banner as its cross,
The National Anthem—the holy hymn.
The Pledge of Allegiance the credo
The riches of the land became Heaven,
The assembly line, the poverty and the prisons—Hell.
The Almighty Dollar became Almighty God,
A God more responsive than Allah or Yahweh to almost any wish.
From the White House and the Capitol,
Prophets reveal new verses every day,
Through the modern Gabriel, the television set.
And the Supreme Court is the Holy See,
Constantly interpreting and reinterpreting the old and new verses,
Separating the innocent from the guilty,
As if the Day of Judgment was at hand."

Asks Hafez: "So this national religion will condemn me
If I take Mitra as my wife, telling me she is not a woman,
But an invented species called Teenager?"

Pirooz nods. "In the eyes of the national religion she is still a child."
Hafez is angry: "But the God of the Holy Books
Does not define Mitra as a child and she does not define herself as child!
What of Free Will? Am I also a child?
My Mitra has read more books than the learned of my times.
She speaks languages I never knew existed and
Visited more of the world than any of the great explorers of my time.
She could teach my worldly grandmother a thing or two
About the most sensuous and intoxicating things, Pirooz Jaan!
Damn all the clergies of all national religions, Pirooz Jaan!
They violate the laws of Nature with their man-made rules.
They suppress the joyful flames of desire with their man-made rules.
They gag and tie willing men and willing women
To invisible posts in the town square with their man-made rules,
So people can't touch or talk, but only see and yearn!
What instruments of torture are these man-made rules?
I say to hell with these man-made rules!"
Rumi is sympathetic: "What a waste, these crushing rules!
This modern world, from what little I have seen of it,
Is a complicated, contradictory, and incongruous place,
Looming with possibilities but brimming with obstacles.
It coddles some with its luxuries and miracle drugs,
Causing them to remain babies inside,
Even as they grow older and older outside.
Meanwhile, it coarsens others with brutality and neglect,
Forcing them to mature faster and faster, aging them fast.
What an injustice it is to treat babies as adults and adults as babies.
And worst of all, in this modern world it seems that
The best seeds are not planted in the best gardens!
The worst seeds have the power and the best seeds the ideas.
Ideas flower ultimately, but only over the graves of their creators."

The apartment is filled with a Sphinx of silence.

Finally Pirooz breaks the silence,
Agreeing with Rumi that, "Yes, the new world is a tough place
To be in love, and to be loved back,
Especially when loyalty is so scarce.
Our machines have ground the ancient mysteries into pulp,
Our medicines have diluted our pain yet also our passions.
The only true love permitted today is the selfish love of self,
So that we, like drone bees and dumbwitted ants
Will work and work and buy and buy
As much as we possibly can until we die."

Pirooz's pessimism makes Hafez shiver.
"But professor," he asks, "haven't you ever been in love?"
This makes Pirooz smile a little, then frown a little,
And run to his bookshelves for a shoebox full of letters.
"Yes," he says, "her name was Iraan,
The same name as our homeland."
He fishes through the box, retrieving a particular letter
Written on raspberry-red paper.
"I wrote this poem to her the night cancer stole her away."
He unfolds the letter, straightens it respectfully, and reads:

"Iraan, Iraan, Iraan Jaan,
Where are you? Iraan Jaan?
Have you not heard my voiceless cries?
That my bed without you is nothing, yes nothing,
But an enormous emptiness that grinds me down
With the savage teeth of loneliness?

"Iraan, Iraan, Iraan Jaan,
Have you not heard the drummer's crazy dance inside my heart?
Whenever I imagine your footsteps behind the gate of time
That scream out in scarlet: 'Don't you ever stop!
Come and fill me, too! Come and fill me, too!'?

"Iraan, Iraan, Iraan Jaan,
If you haven't seen the flames of my indefatigable love for you,
Then surely you have been journeying alone, yes alone,
To distant places and loveless times.
I am going to weave a net, Iraan Jaan,
As extensive as all imaginations combined,
And cast it into the future to capture all the years unborn,
Before they speed away with you and me still apart.

"I'll find you, Iraan Jaan, where the blue sky and the blue sea
Become the same seamless world
And the setting sun baptizes all worlds."

Hafez feels himself feeling better,
Feeling hope, that there is still hope for his love, and for all love
In this mad and mean modern world.
"Was this Iraan your greatest love, Pirooz?
This woman who inspired you to write with such deep emotion?"
Pirooz folds the letter and slips it back into the shoebox.
"If she was, I will be grateful and satisfied,
For Iraan was truly wonderful.
But I still hope, dear Hafez, that my greatest love is yet to come,
That my ultimate love is still hiding like a goddess in my mind."
"Ah," sighs Rumi, "tell us about this love."
For this love Pirooz does not need words already written.
These words are already written in his heart.
He closes his eyes and recites:

"Surrounded by parched grass and withered roses,
While the sun gazes at my loneliness with its burning eyes,
I wish a miracle, for my perfect love to emerge and
For the blue sky to rain happiness on us.

"But my loneliness is thirsty, too!
It gazes at me and sips my imagination,
Thought by thought, demand by demand.
Yes, destructive as a one-sided love,
Vicious as all the enemies of mankind combined,
My longings suck my spirit dry, drop by drop, ache by ache.

"Now I see a white dove against the dead blue-black sky.
I become attached to the dove, hoping it brings
A message from my imaginary love.
But soon, too soon, the dove is gone,
Except for my expectations which, like a feather, it has left behind.
And so my longings rush back like a betrayed lover,
Glowering at me and raging at me with a blazing gaze.

"I run from those glowering eyes.
I run from the eyes of my own demanding mind,
Staring at me in the mirror of my mind, asking:
'Where is the perfect love you keep in your mind?'
And I run also from the crowds,
Which only accentuate my loneliness,
Until I descend into the valley of despair.
And even as despair renders me blind,
I still look for the one I've lost before she could be found."

Hafez nods: "This perfect love you lost before you found
Is the same perfect love I sought for centuries,
And have just now found in the backseat of my taxi—
My most-perfect Mitra!
So there is still hope for you and your perfect love, Pirooz Jaan.
Be content with God's will, his plodding and difficult terms."
Pirooz bristles: "You want me to praise God
For keeping from me the love that makes me whole?
If anything, I should yell at him,

'What are you waiting for? Hurry up!'"

Pirooz's outburst both surprises and delights Hafez.

"There is no need to yell at God, at me, or anyone else.

'God's will' is just an expression.

I was merely telling you to be patient."

BOOK TWO:

Poem of Poems

8 The Poem Of Poems

Saturday dawns,
Causing true Manhattanites to yawn and stretch and rejoice
That the busy bridge-and-tunnel people
Won't be coming to the island today.
Yes, on Saturday the city transcends its weekday fanaticism,
Becoming a small and wonderful town.
Pirooz fixes Rumi and Hafez an American breakfast,
Pancakes and scrambled eggs, and suggests to them that,
"Today would be a good day to do nothing."

And so the professor and the two poets set out to do nothing:
They sit in the basement laundry room reading old magazines
While the machines spin and goosh,
Hafez reveling that people today
Fold their sheets exactly as they did a thousand years ago;
Then they go upstairs and sit on Pirooz's long sofa and watch TV,
Giving each channel just seconds to impress them
Before they click to the next.
They nap, the snores of one drowning the snores of the others,
So that everyone is able to sleep.
Finally, when they have completely run out of nothing to do,
They stand side-by-side at the window, magpies on a naked limb,
Looking ten floors down to Riverside Drive,
And the park sloping down to the highway,
And to the Hudson River flowing beyond.

It is all so big, it is all so small.
The trucks and cars are cats and mice,
The boats, bobbing seagulls, the barges, runaway twigs.

The people are but wingless sparrows,
Hopping this way and that, everywhere.
The treetops seem as close to the ground as the grass,
The mighty Hudson looks no bigger than a brook.
Says Pirooz of the view: "This is the work of a perfectionist painter,
Who forever modifies his unfinished works
With new hues, shapes, minds, and sounds,
One day hiding the sunlight with dark clouds,
The next day dispersing them with one brush,
To reveal the moonlight and the midnight.
One day the painter spanks the summer trees with rain,
Only to change his mind the next,
Dipping the green leaves into psychedelic paintpots,
Letting them dance to the disappearing ground.
Then he changes his mind again
And sugars everything with chill,
One day he paints the sky Plato's perfect blue,
The next he dulls it with the kaleidoscopic fumes
Spewing from those factory facades,
Jig-jagging like broken teeth on the New Jersey shore.
Yes! This is the work of a perfectionist painter
Who mixes the inventions of man with the inventiveness of Nature."

Rumi asks Pirooz: "And just who is this masterful painter?"
Pirooz protests with a smile, saying,
"Rumi Jaan, I thought we were going to do nothing today?
If I answer Science, you will answer God,
And we will do nothing today but argue."

They watch a carefree girl chase a carefree balloon.
They watch a bus cough to a stop, spitting out a row of dominoes.
They watch a plane fly low enough to catch a fish.
"What a strange gallery this is," Pirooz says.
"We stand still while the paintings march by."

Hafez replies: "Then let us take some wine and food,
And rush to the river and become part of the painting."
"The river is dead," Pirooz informs them glumly.
"But we are not dead!" Rumi and Hafez respond together.

The three Persians pack a picnic in a hurry and
Crowd into the cranky elevator and descend into the painting.
They cross Riverside Drive—disregarding the horn blowers—
And trot down the stone steps into the park.
They pass a playground brimming with laughter,
Pass empty green benches and an ice cream vendor's
Mouth-watering, ring-a-ling bell.
They tiptoe across the dangerous paths of rollerbladers,
Smiling at two lovers locked in each other's arms.
They pass stray dogs barking and weary beggars begging.
They pass an underpass and march on toward the Hudson.

A muddy path leads them through a swath of yellowy weeds,
Toward a huddle of boulders.
They encounter beer cans and broken bottles, single lost shoes,
Hamburger wrappers clinging to thistles,
Rotting tires that once rolled along on highways,
Discarded bricks once the pretty face of a millionaire's home.
They reach the boulders and carefully step over them,
As if they were balls of burning lava.

Hafez is heartbroken.
From Pirooz's window these boulders
Appeared to be the guardians of truth and beauty,
Whose sturdy backs one could perch upon
And admire Mankind and Naturekind,
As they mixed and melded and flowed in harmony.
But now he sees that these boulders are only pallbearers,

Carrying the dead river on their shoulders,
In a sad and somber funeral procession,
Just as the deep river carries the ghosts of dead fish.
The funeral march is accompanied not by a somber dirge,
But by rock-and-roll blaring from passing cars.
The path is not decorated with the petals of roses,
But colorless poisons disgorging from the sewer pipes of modernity.

Hafez cries out: "It all looked so magnificent from above!"
"Modernity from a distance is very pretty," Pirooz answers.
"But up close it can be deadly, especially if unchecked—
A rabid beaver devouring the evolutionary tree.
Man used to fear Nature but now Nature must fear Man."

Rumi suggests they should go back to Pirooz's apartment,
Saying that, "Paintings always look better from a distance."
But Hafez shakes his head. "Mowlana, if this is a funeral,
We need to stay and mourn."
So the three Persians, though filled with grief,
Open the wine and fill up their paper cups, and drink and drink,
To drown the bittersweet taste of modernity.
Mumbles Pirooz: "I wonder what the river thinks of Man?
What the witnessing stars think of Man?"
Rumi looks up at the crimson clouds and squints, and listens,
Thinking he can hear the river's whimpering cries
As it endures Modernity's endless thrusts.
He wipes his teary eyes and with a somber voice asks Pirooz,
"Has modernity poisoned poetry, too, professor?"
Pirooz shrugs, and says: "Not yet."

As they drink and reach for pears and apples,
A thunderbolt blows the clouds apart, unveiling a rainbow.
Freed, the rainbow divides in two
And flaps like the joined wings of a bird—until it is a bird.

As the three Persians gaze in amazement, the bird swoops down,
Perching on Rumi's uplifted knee.
A halo surrounds the bird's feathery head,
As if it were a saint with colored wings.
"I am the Poem of Poems," declares the bird.
"Like the King of Kings!
I am real but not real,
Mythical yet I can appear with bones and flesh.
I am like the Persian Simorgh who could cure all diseases.
I am like the Egyptian phoenix, death is a new life for me.
I am like the Hoopoe bird of Attar who leads the many,
To the unity of Onemany.
I am the summation of human experiences
And the expression of human aspirations.
I will speak for poems—all poems in all tongues.
And I will speak for poets and poetry, too!
Yes, I am the Poem of Poems:
My ear is the wind—I hear everything.
My eye is the sun—I see everything.
My tongue is history—it sings the same in different languages.
My body is the earth—I hold everyone in my arms.
My veins are rivers—nourishing all who come to me.
My heart is the palpitating sea—kissing shore after shore,
As the naked moon walks sexily across the deep blue sky.
My spirit is the fire that delights—not the fire that burns.
Time is my ship and the universe is my ocean.
My home is where I happen to be.
Words are my neurons, and
Alas, sentences are my prison!"

Pirooz puts down his cup of wine.
"Are you real or are we really drunk?"
The Poem of Poems laughs and says:
"Oh, you are drunk enough, but I am also real enough.

To those I favor I can be seen and heard, even touched.
My fragrance rises from Hafez's odes,
Wherever he plants a narcissus or a rose.
I am a painting that sings music composed of words,
I am the music composed of words, not notes.
I am meaning with rhythm and rhythm with meaning.
I am a dardedel cuddled by the souls,
The philosophy that tangos with psychology.
I am sociology without the jibber-jabber,
A story written by stars on the empty blue."

"My tail is rhyme," the bird tells the three Persians.
"It sweeps the dictionary with wide-open eyes!
I am the love child and the hate child,
Of both the real and imagined worlds.
I can be a lunatic, nasty, erotic,
Moody, witty, silly, obscene, profane, lovely, kindly and wise,
Even informative, even revolutionary,
All depending, all depending.
I remember the future, I imagine the past,
I think in a present that has no bounds.
I am the widow of dead dreams.
Like an empty oven, I can be very sad,
I can be happy as a wedding,
As hopeful and helpful and bright as a lighthouse,
When dark tiger waves threaten little lost boats."

When at last the bird stops, Rumi asks: "Poem of Poems,
You have told us who and what you are,
But where do you come from?"
"Mowlana," coos the bird, as a lover might,
"Who knows how or why or when my beginning began?
I was born before history, sometime during the ancient twilight,
When baby language was wet—no diaper yet—and

Cried out for the mother-god's milk!
Perhaps I was the rhythmic string of magic words
Sung to induce the Yam Yam tree to bear more Yam Yams!
Perhaps I was the first love song of Man
When he tried to imitate the love songs of birds.
Or perhaps I was a primitive prayer,
Chanted to thwart thunderbolts from forests and caves,
To ward off fear in the heart of human existence.
No wonder most gods speak with rhythm and even rhyme!
It is all in the Holy Books—read, read, and read!"

The bird now tells them how, little by little, poems
Became songs to tell others how one existed, thought, or felt,
How little by little, as man established moral and aesthetic order,
Political, social, and cultural order,
Man also established Poetic Order.
Pirooz could not agree more, saying:
"In every language, language was turned into a sword—
To intimidate! To chain! To exploit!"

The bird continues:
"As time passed, my feathers were chained
By grammar, by syntax, by uneasy spellings,
By transfixed rules of rhyme, rhythm and meter,
And by the militaristic way words were lined up on paper,
Even by Hafez, even by Rumi, as he himself complained.
Everything became as rigid as death.
I was no longer allowed to pick whatever seed—
Whatever word, I mean—that I desired.
The dictionaries that were imprinted
In the minds of the ancients were mutilated!
Some words were banished, some set on fire!
Ideas and emotions uncomfortable to kings became taboo.
Man could not even mention his own private parts in poems

Without fear of having them cut off!
I was put in a cage and the door was slammed shut.
My eyes were filled with sand, my ears with molten lead,
And my beak sewed tight with threads of iron.
As the centuries went by chains were added to my chains,
And my cage was put in a cage.
Vicious dogs of tradition encircled me, round and round,
Preventing not only escape,
But even the thought of escape."
"How true," Hafez interrupts.
"Often I had to dissimulate, or compromise,
Or compose in voices mysterious even to myself.
Oh, those useless words I used to rhyme, just to rhyme,
Hound me even in death!"
Rumi agrees: "I often complained in my own poems
Of such rigid rules, called *Aruz* in Persian.
Still, I obeyed Aruz as if it were the word of God!"

The Poem of Poems goes on:
"Poetry became more and more rigid.
In Persia the themes of Hafez were used and re-used forever.
Until even my prison guards were poets!"

The magnificent bird lifts its head and opens its beak,
As if breathing in inspiration.
"Then modernity was born—*Ooooh!* What a difficult birth!
New science and technology expanded human possibilities,
Opening eyes, heightening human consciousness,
Causing revolutions in minds, modes of learning, working and living.
People took power, banishing kings and lords,
Restricting the reach of the clergy,
Liberating slaves, serfs, and women,
Even I was liberated—to fly free and sing in verses free,
From China to Persia, from Africa to America,

From Europe to Everywhere!
Oh, I've kept a few of my chains, just to remember—see!"
The Poem of Poems takes to the air, showing the three Persians
The short silver links dangling from its feather tips.
As it dances in the wind the remaining chains collide,
Ching ching ching.
And the bird sings: "The chains are torn, I am free verse at last!
Swing bird, swing—no strings, no kings, no slings.
The world has opened and is open wide.
So choose how you wish to sing, and ding and fling!
Free at last! Free at last! Poems and poets are free at last!
To be what they wish to be, to become what they wish to become."
The bird soars higher, twisting its chains around its breast,
Ching ching ching.
It sings so loud the Persians fear all of Manhattan will hear,
And rush to the river to see if elephants are dancing on the river:

The Poem of Poems sings: "Rejoice and rejoice,
No word is banished or forced to march like soldiers on the page.
Pages are no longer prison cells or cemetery rows.
Pages are now floors for liberated words and ideas to dance upon,
So be free and happy and dance and dance.
No rhyme, no rhythm, no meter,
No Peter or Paul intervening.
Rejoice and rejoice for language and languages,
For dictionaries and thesauruses
As big as dinosaurases,
As wide open as imaginations.
Rejoice for the literary, the spoken, the super-cool colloquial.
The white tongue, the black tongue, all tongues, all tongues.
Rejoice and rejoice, for unchained forms and contents,
Expressions, metaphors, and meanings.
The demeaned word is not the forbidden word.
Poets are no longer guards guarding themselves.

Poets now are seers, chroniclers, revered revolutionaries,
Reveling in the freedom of free verse.
Rejoice and rejoice for liberty has invited souls of every shape and color
To come around and compose whatever poems they wish,
However they wish.
Classicism, romanticism, symbolism, modernism, postmodernism,
All isms, all isms, all isms,
Have come alive like candlelight through pretty prisms,
To enlighten the path and frighten the shadows away.
Rejoice and rejoice for poetry of fact and investigative poetry,
For all have come to my liberty party,
And despite their differences
All are having the time of their lives:
'Another cup of liberty tea, good friend?'
'Of course, yes of course, yes of course!'"

Now the bird swoops low, landing square on Rumi's head,
Lamenting: "But soon the rejoicing was over.
There was no more tea or thunderlaughs,
No chinging or changing or chunging.
Poets, it seems, wanted even more freedom!
They wanted to crash through the final obstacles,
To touch the earliest reality where only pictures existed."
Rumi, baffled, rolls his eyes skyward,
Trying to see the mysterious bird through his white bushy eyebrows.
"Poetry without words? That is like trying to whistle without lips,
Or dance without feet!"

The Poem of Poems digs his toes into the Mowlana's scalp,
Soliciting an unpoetic *Ouch!*
Then it continues: "The poets' new grief was that
The world of words was tiny when compared
To the immense inner world of imagination,
And the limitless outer world of reality.

So much of both worlds was still unobserved and unworded!
Even the world of the unconscious, the very womb of creativity,
Was left unconscious!"

Hafez, fearing the sharp-toed bird will settle on his head next,
Shrinks his neck and mumbles,
"How ironic, Poem of Poems, you have put into words
Something I felt all my mortal life!"
The bird punishes Hafez's interruption
With another dig at Rumi's head,
Which makes Pirooz laugh and spit his wine.
The bird sighs and goes on:
"The language that once distinguished man from animals
Was now a barrier to the creative self-realization of man.
So a poet complained: 'Language thinks for me,
Instead of me thinking for me!'
And the poet was right!
Language was invented for practical matters,
Like hunting and gathering and making fire.
It was never meant to be precise or attend to the soul.
Words are abstract! Words are fuzzy!
To describe the sky man could only say blue.
To describe a poppy man could only say red.
Yes, as liquid as man's language was,
It could never describe all the shades of all the colors,
All sounds, fragrances, tastes, or soft touches.
So poets used symbols—drawings, photographs, numbers—
To describe a face, a smile, a mood, a melody,
A situation, an autumn, or a mango,
More precisely than any word or words could do.
They called this poetry *concrete poetry*, saying,
'If words can picture a scene, then surely pictures can picture words.'
And it was not just the old taboo subjects discussed,
But new subjects that never existed,

Not in ancient times nor even ten seconds ago!
The coming of computers stimulated *cyberpoets*,
Whose poems, while easy to look at
Are nearly impossible to describe or discern."

Rumi not only hears the bird's words, but feels its passion:
"Show me what you mean, Poem of Poems,
So that I will know what you mean."
This time the bird does not dig its toes into the poet's head,
But bends its neck and gently kisses his brow.
"As you wish, Mowlana!"
It stands tall and puffs its breast.
From its parting beak a beam of light pierces the sky,
Turning a black cloud white, displaying a poem already written:

Life is a many sum game

Sometime it adds up—sometimes it doesn't

Poker is a *zero* sum game

What I lose is what you win

Love is a *positive* sum game

A kiss for you is a kiss for me

War is a *negative* sum game

The loser loses and the winner loses

Now tell me who wants to play

Which game and why?

The three Persians applaud and plead, "More! More! More!"
Until a new poem appears:

Man,
Are you watching watches
Or are watches watching you?
Man,

Did you make the machine
Or is the machine making you?
Man,
Do you feel the termites of greed
Chewing at your body and soul?
Man,
Just who's on watch here?
You or something bigger than you?
Man,
Wake up before you can never wake up
Man.

When the Persians want more,
The Poem of Poem opens his beak as wide as it will go,
And boldly flashes across the silver cloud:

$$E=mc^2$$

While Hafez gasps, and Rumi scratches his head,
Pirooz claps his hands and cheers.
He is enchanted that the Poem of Poems has chosen
This famous formula as a *poem*.
He lifts his arms to the poem and tells them,
"It is the most concise description of nature ever written."
"That is quite a reputation for such a tiny poem to shoulder," says Rumi.
"Tell us, professor, can you translate it for us?"
Pirooz nods and promises to try:
"The energy within a mass equals the same mass,
Times the speed of light
Times the speed of light . . .
In other words, a very small thing can make a lot of heat."

"Ahhhh!" says Hafez. "Who wrote this marvelous poem?"

Answers Pirooz: "His name was Einstein and
He composed the poem thinking he was composing science.
In the modern world there are many poets
Unaware that they are poets."

Though as full of wine as Rumi and Hafez,
Pirooz cannot easily accept the presence of a talking bird
Flashing poems on the clouds, as if its beak was a movie projector.
"What exactly is your mission?" he asks.
The Poem of Poems hops off Rumi's head
And into Pirooz's surprised arms,
Singing as quietly as a sparrow might:
"To make pain more bearable, Pirooz Jaan,
To bridge the divide between *me* and *you*, *us* and *them*.
I am a hand reaching for the unreachable.
I am a duration between two vast waitings:
Waiting for birth and waiting for death.
I glue people, times, and places together.
I am all poems together.
Poets did compose me, but I did compose poets, too,
For poets now must drink from my breast
Before they can compose!"
"Drink from your breast?" Pirooz asks with a sly smile.
"You are a bird! Birds don't have milk!"
The Poem of Poems turns its head sideways,
The way birds do, and winking a big bird eye, says,
"Professor! If I am not allowed to wax poetically, then who is?"

The three Persians' laughter is suddenly muffled
By a thunderous flapping of wings as
The bird leaps from Pirooz's arms.
Now hovering just out of his reach, it says,
"My mission is to clarify and verify the attributes of existence,
Distinguishing beauty from ugliness,

In all their respective shades and disguises.
My mission is to glorify truth and love and peace,
To purify the human soul.
My mission is to cry out, to defy,
Injustice and prejudice,
To shatter the chains that restrict imagination and creation.
My mission is to induce smiles, understandings, and dreams.
I magnify! I mystify! I unify!
I satisfy deep longings!
I am you and you are me!"

The poem of Poems begins to flap furiously,
Chains colliding, *ching ching ching*.
Even as it fights to break free of gravity, it sings:
"I am a bundle of contradictions in flight!
When poems collide within me, cultures collide like sperm and egg,
And a new unexpected understanding is conceived.
I enlist all senses! I summon all souls!
I say the unsayable! I soar as high as I wish!"

The Poem of Poems is suddenly gone
And the river bank washed with the shadow of a man.
The three Persians turn to find a policeman tapping his nightstick.
"This is no place for a picnic," he warns. "Move along, move along."
And so they head home to Pirooz's apartment,
Stunned and astonished by the magic of the day.
Rumi and Pirooz discuss the crazy traffic,
How so many people can be going in different directions all at once.
But Hafez does not join in, cannot join in.
He is thinking of Mitra,
How the effervescent Poem of Poems reminded him of her,
How in two lives, and one long death in between,
He has never missed anything as he now misses his Mitra Jaan.

9   There's No Place Like Home

Hafez is back at Pirooz's window
Watching the park police chase other people away.
"How far has mankind fallen," he moans,
"That picnics are illegal?"
Explains Pirooz with a chuckle,
"Picnics are still legal, Hafez Jaan.
But night is falling,
And the night brings out people who do illegal things.
The policeman was only protecting us."
Hafez does not understand:
"Then the policeman should have guarded us until
Our wine was gone and our basket empty.
And then walked us home."

While Pirooz and Rumi play a game of chess,
Hafez continues to gaze from the window,
Seeing the city's skyline as a battlefield,
New York and God warring,
One for light,
One for night.
"New York shelters all but is home to none," he says.
"Nevertheless, I did adopt New York," answers Pirooz,
One check away from mating the Mowlana.
"And New York did adopt me.
Just like you and the city of Shiraz adopted each other, Hafez!
Though I curse my fate, and sometimes delude myself,
The truth is that this city and I are family now—no matter what."

Hafez turns from the window. "Tell me, professor,

"Just how did you and this city come to adopt each other?"
Pirooz answers this way: "When a school boy in Teheran,
I could not watch a despot and not cry foul.
But I feared arrest and torture, so
For safety I ran far away from Iran.
Then theocratic rule came to my homeland,
With clergymen proclaiming the ultimate Truth.
The mullahs, it seemed, loved the dead, hated the living,
Declaring the Day of Judgment before God was ready.
They banished whoever claimed:
'I see, I hear, I think, and choose to reject
All that is false, immoral and ugly.'
To scrub scriptures of intolerance you have to scrub
Religions out of minds."
Pirooz waves off playing a second game.
"Anyway, here I am in New York,
Free of Iran's despots and mullahs,
Exasperated by America claiming to be more than it is,
While claiming others are worse than they are."
Seeing that his guests are saddened by his sadness,
Pirooz puts on a grin and asks: "Tell me, my prickly friends,
Was it your own decision to come alive in America?
You could have counted stars in the salty desert of Dasht-e Kavir
Just as well as in the Sonora—is it not the same sky?"

Hafez replies: "When God granted us our wish to return to life,
So we could count the stars and see the vastness of His creation,
Our first choice was indeed Dasht-e Kavir.
But as we made our way toward Heaven's gilded gates,
We met so many Persians coming the other way,
Passing into death from life.
They told us what you have told us, Pirooz Jaan,
How the mullahs cursed music, dance, wine, chess, beauty, happiness,
Bashing women back into dark veils and dark times,

Forcing everyone to mourn and mourn for the ancient martyrs.
Though free from pain or repression ourselves,
We still could not bear to witness such tragedies,
To hear the chants and the screams
Wafting across the salty sand as we tried to count.
So, like so many living Persians today,
We migrated to America, to the clear skies of Arizona.
How tragic it is, Pirooz Jaan, that so many Persians,
Both dead and living, are in Diaspora—
Not because of the foreign occupation of Iran,
But because of the clergy's occupation of Iran."

Rumi, in the kitchen,
Opening and closing the refrigerator door,
Trying to see if the light inside goes out when the door closes,
Or stays lit to warm the cold food,
Now joins the conversation,
His face going bright and dark, bright and dark
As he works the refrigerator door:
"But even from the Sonora, disguised as saguaros,
We could not escape the pain and tumult of our countrymen.
"But feel no sorrow for us, Pirooz Jaan.
Meeting you in the desert has proven most serendipitous.
We saved you from you while doing some sightseeing on the side."
Hafez spins dervishly: "And don't forget about my Mitra!
Finding her in my taxi is the most serendipitous of all!"

Rumi gives up and joins the others.
The refrigerator is simply too fast for him.
"Hafez running after Mitra with his taxi
Reminds me of something I wrote ages ago:

Intoxicated by love and impelled by desire,
Last night I was scurrying in bewilderment

102

In every direction."

Pirooz looks at his watch and proclaims:
"The day that was to be nothing,
Is turning out to be really something.
Shall we dardedel a little, and make it last forever?"
Rumi and Hafez settle on Pirooz's blue satin couch.
(Blue is the favorite color of Persians:
The color of the most precious stones,
The color of tiles in the little fish pools,
The indescribable blue of holy inscriptions
In the great mosques.)

Pirooz puts on a CD and smiles
As the magic notes of Lotfi's' tar revitalizes his heart.
He sits across from the two poets,
In his favorite saffron-yellow chair.
On the glass-top table between them
Rests a crystal vase of red roses,
A bronze dish piled high with pistachios,
A tall bottle of purple wine
And a candle as green as a rice stalk.

Rumi reaches for a handful of the nuts,
Their shells split like the mouths of tiny clams.
"These modern American pistachios taste almost as good
As the ancient pistachios I ate as a boy," he says.
His voice is so filled with joy, that it seems to Pirooz
He is singing the lyrics Lotfi always intended.
"They are grown in America," Pirooz says,
"By growers from Persia.
Their taste has an accent, like Persian art, Persian words,
Persian feelings, and Persian thoughts in America.
Like me and you, these pistachios live in Diaspora!

But they are damn good, aren't they?
Just like your poems, Mowlana!
Your poems are deformed by translation, true,
And accented by foreign minds, true,
But they are still damn good and true!
They pour goodness into the heart and ethos of America.
The soul of Persia nourishes the soul of America.
The souls fuse while the rulers refuse!"

"By the way, Pirooz," Rumi says as he munches,
That strange bird, that Poem of Poems,
Flew off without telling us about the poetry of Iran.
Can you fill us in?"
Pirooz is astonished. "But don't you know this already?"
Rumi is astonished that Pirooz is astonished.
"One dies with what one knows.
And in death one learns no more
About the world left behind—
Unless God grants you a reprieve and
Sends you back to learn what is new.
Now speak to us of poetry, Pirooz Jaan."
"I am not a poetry expert," Pirooz cautions.
The wine in Hafez's belly swirls as he laughs.
"Birds are not poetry experts either!
You do read Persian poetry, do you not, Pirooz?"

Pirooz is giddy with exhilaration that fate
Is allowing him to lecture these two immortal poets
About the poets they themselves spawned,
As if they were two eager freshmen with empty heads.
"Yes—every night I read Persian poetry!
They are my wine, my warm glass of milk,
My home away from home."
Now he pulls himself from his chair and advances

104

Dizzily to his book shelves.
He fills his arms and returns to his chair and his glass of wine.
He thumbs excitedly through one of his books.
"I will read you a few samples, as examples
Of modern Persian poetry."
Pirooz opens one of his books,
And with the help of the spittle on his finger,
Finds the page he wants.
"This is a poem by Yushij,
Considered the father of modern Persian verse.
He shattered the old rigid themes and reformed the form
By untying the knots of rhyme and introducing new meter.

'O people,
Who are giddy
And giggling on the seaside.
Look, someone is drowning,
Gasping for air, fighting for life—
In the wolfish, dark waves
Of the heavy seas
When you are drunk
With delusions of victories . . . .'"

Pirooz finds another page in the same book.
"Shamlu, a disciple of Yushij,
Was an indefatigable poet and fighter for freedom.
A mere nineteen years old, he was a political prisoner
When his father asked him to write
A letter of remorse to the authorities to secure his release.
This is part of his poem, called 'Letter':

'O father,
Do you ask me to be a coward,
To repent and bow to the enemy,

To choose deceit over truth—
To shackle my soul
Just to unshackle my body?
You take yourself to safety, father,
And I take myself
To the battlefield—to danger!'"

Hafez finds a tear meandering down his cheek
And flicks it away, saying in a whisper,
"This Shamlu is very brave."
Pirooz, nodding, finds yet another page.
"Shamlu criticizes the poetry of the past
For not being poetry for the people.
Listen to this one, it is called 'Poetry Which Is Life':

'Today poems are the
Weapons of the masses,
For poets are
Trees in the forests
Of the masses,
And not jasmine, or,
Hyacinth blossoming in
Someone's flower garden.'"

Pirooz now reads bits and pieces of Shamlu's poems,
Revealing with his enthusiasm
His love and awe for the poet's way with words,
And his way with courage.
"Just listen to this—it is called 'Aida in the Mirror':

'Delicate as poems
Your lips twirl the most
Hedonistic kiss
Into such unheard coyness,

Apt to transmute
The burrowing beast
Into a human!'

"And this:
Your body is a melody,
And my body is the lyric
That locks into yours
To make a song
Of palpitating continuity!'"

"And listen to this from
'The Rain's Travelogue':

'The last words
Of a raindrop were:
Filthy is the earth!'"

Rumi and Hafez beg Pirooz to continue,
Even though the wine has turned his lips into rubber,
And the black sky outside has divided his breath into yawns.
Says Pirooz: "Then came the young woman Farrokhzad,
Who, like her poems, never grew old.
She was caught between tradition and modernity,
And trapped in a loveless marriage,
The fate of so many Eastern women,
The wedding ring their master's chain.
Forced to choose between her son and her lover,
She complains in a poem called 'Sin':

'You, my love, are the sky—
Luminous and pure
I am a bird captured in a trap.
O sky, what if I try to fly

One day away from this
Prison—stilled, cold, and stern.
What am I to tell
The tearful eyes of my child:
That I am a captive bird
[That must flee]
So forget about me!'

"She wishes her lover who is not her husband to take her
From the city of sorrow to the zenith of passion.
And once the forbidden love is consummated, she confesses:

'Yes, I have sinned
A titillating sin
In his enflamed embrace
Devoured in his arms
I have sinned.
Inside his unforgettable arms
Sizzling like a red rod
I have sinned!'

Hafez takes the book from Pirooz.
"Do not put this one away, professor.
I must read it to my Mitra!"

Pirooz now tells them of Sepehri.
"He was a poet and painter of extraordinary sensitivity,
Who journeyed far away to the Far East
And drank from the spirit of
Taoism, Confucianism and Buddhism.
In a long masterpiece called 'The Sound of Water's Footsteps'
He speaks of his observations:

'I saw the people

I saw the cities
The plains and the mountains.
I saw the earth and the water,
The light and the darkness,
And saw the plants in the light
And the plants in the dark
And animals in the light
And animals in the dark.
I saw humans in the light
And humans in the dark.
I saw, I saw . . .
That the wings of life
Are as widespread as death
That life can leap
As high as love
That life is not a thing
To be placed on the shelf of routine,
And be forgotten by you and me!
We,
Must wash our eyes clean
Must see the world in a different light
Must bathe the words
Must close the umbrella
Must go under the rainfall
Must take the memories,
And the thoughts
Under the rainfall.
All must stand together
Under the rainfall,
Must seek love under the rainfall,
Must play, write, talk
And plant lilies under the rainfall.
Life is being soaked again and again.
Life is splashing around

In the pool of the present.'

Pirooz smiles: "Now here are a few lines
by my exiled friend, Esma'il Kho'i.
It is called 'My Home In A Suitcase.'

'Where is my home?
For what am I homesick?
    I ask
         myself
                Now and then
And who is my friend
Whom am I longing for?

'Your message is ringing in my ears still:
You're no longer safe at home!
And your advice:
For God's sake hurry, depart!

'What have I done?
Except listen to your advice
And consequently now
Fallen into the abyss of silence
And neglect.'

Pirooz reads more and more until he sees Rumi's yawn
Spread to the lips of Hafez.
He smiles apologetically, and says:
"I know you are tired and hundreds
Of wonderful poets' poems must be reviewed to get the whole story.
But I will end with the ending of a poem called 'Loving,'
By my friend and star, Naderpour:

'O beloved afar

Now that a world
Separates us
Could I see you
In my dreams?
Or like a shadow lay
Beside you in my awakenings?
Would I
In the astonishing moment
Of unity with you,
Once more whisper your sweet name
In your ears?
I wish that in the darkness of the night that
Took you away from me
I would have perished
In the fragrance of your exotic hair
I wish that on the same night
From your side
I would have been
Whirled to the side
Of annihilation!'"

Rumi breaks his silence: "What poems!
No candles, no flame burning the lover moth,
No jug-bearer of wine capturing lovers' hearts.
No fauna and flora that eternity abide.
No bleeding nightingales singing love songs
To thorny, needling roses.
No praising of prophets and their dreams.
What changes! What changes!
Raindrops calling the earth filthy,
Sons accepting prison rather than their fathers' advice,
Women longing openly for forbidden sex,
Common people called to rise against their kings."

Hafez is equally astonished: "How wonderful!
Poems composed for the people,
And not for patrons, conquerors or other poets
With nothing better to do with their time
Than soak their feet, sing songs and eat figs!
Everything in these new poems is touched!
Sometimes rough, yet right.
Sometimes tough, yet loving.
Times are so different.
Minds are so different.
Love is so different.
Poems are so different.
And I am becoming so different hearing them!"
"Yes, yes," Rumi agrees, "But still . . ."
"But still, what?" asks Pirooz,
Watching the Mowlana's eyes flutter until they are closed.
Rumi answers: "But still I want to hear the sound of a Nay,
Those wonderful flutes whittled from hollow marsh reeds."
And so Pirooz obliges and changes the disc
And as the ancient woody notes echo
From the disk's modern grooves,
Rumi sings as if to himself:
"I have had two lives but only one death!
My death was in a bed in one room in one city.
My lives spread over the world and history."
Now the new words spilling from his wine-stained lips
Give way to old words from old poems:

'Come to us
Bring music to us
Rise! Let us beat the drums
And have a celebration here.
I am God, let us say yes.
Our souls are in ecstasy, yes

Intoxicated, but not from wine
But by love and music.

'My brother, you are all intellect
The rest of you is flesh and bones
The soul of this world we are—
Not just bodies, sagging and perishing,
We are not bound to earth
We are spirits
Love is our mother
We are born out of love!
Love is the most wondrous temptation
Worship love, my friend,
All else is nothing but wind
Love means farewell to reason
Today is the day of farewell
The day of farewell is today!'"

By the time Rumi finishes Hafez is already asleep.
So Pirooz pulls off the old poet's shoes
And covers him with an afghan
And blows out the candle.
He offers Rumi his own bed and,
Taking a blanket and pillow for himself,
Curls up on the floor, at the master's feet.
Although the floor boards are hard,
And the two poets are making the sounds of the locomotives
Not yet invented when they were mortal men,
Pirooz nevertheless sleeps soundly
As if in his boyhood home in Iran,
On a soft bed of belongingness.

10 Slam At The Sad Ghazal

Tonight Pirooz promises to take Hafez and Rumi
To Greenwich Village, to the Sad Ghazal,
To the Friday night poetry slam,
Where poets compete,
Like sumo wrestlers compete,
Until only one is left inside the holy ring.
"You have been promising to take us for weeks," says Hafez.
"Tonight you are actually going to do it?"
"Yes," answers Pirooz,
"Tonight I am finally brave enough to
Read my poems to strangers—
If I can make a fool of myself in front of
The Great Rumi and the Great Hafez,
Why should I fear a roomful of strangers?"

And so they go, in Hafez's cab,
The entire time Hafez lamenting that
Mitra's mother would not let her come along.
"'You may not go out with him,' she said to Mitra,
"'Not tonight, not in a thousand years!'"
Says Pirooz: "You cannot blame a mother for not wanting
Her teenage daughter to go out with a cabbie."
"Or with a poet!" adds Rumi.

The Sad Ghazal is as dark inside
As the November night outside,
And filled to the gills with people and
Steaming cups of espresso and cappuccino.
The three Persians zigzag across the coffee house until

They find a tiny table by the kitchen door.
Far across the room is a small stage, lighted by a single light.
There is a stool and a microphone.
To haphazard applause, a man with beady eyes and small ears
Takes the stage and welcomes everyone.
"I know this man," Pirooz whispers to Rumi and Hafez.
"He is a professor who knows everything about poetry,
Except how to read it or write it.
Oh how dull his lectures are!
Every term he chases a dozen bright students out of liberal arts!"

The Dull Professor introduces the first poet,
A young woman with hair so wild and flying
That she looks like an uprooted onion.
She immediately begins a poem she calls
"Clock Shop Inside":

"Tick-tock, tick-tock,
Every cell has a clock.
From head to toe bio-clocks tick-tock.
Sperm meets Ovum in the nick of time, tick-tock.

"Tick-tock, tick-tock
Gene clocks evolved even behind the knees
To tell the one with luck
The best and safest time-chunk
To sleep, to forage, to mate,
Even when to age and then click-clunk.

"From simple quartz to sizzling quarks,
From the planets to the stars,
To palpitating hearts,
Everything is a clock,
Ticking and ticking and wearing away.

Even love is a clock,
A sad clock that runs out,
A crazy clock that runs amok,
When all its hands—
The I'll-love-you-forever hand,
The until-death-do-us-part hand—
Gets stuck, gets stuck,
Like a dead coo-coo in a rusted clock.
My clock lusts to tick and tock backwards
To find the grandfather clock of all clocks,
At the first tick of time."

As firecracker applause fills the coffee house,
Rumi leans toward Pirooz's ear, whispering:
"Wait until she dies and discovers that
There is no such thing as time—only the endless now."
"Now is endless here, too," Pirooz whispers back.

The next poet is an ebony man
With dreadlocks to the middle of his back.
He speaks in steel-drum Caribbean English,
His words as finely chopped as sugar cane.
He has entitled his poem "I Hid Inside the Smile of Mr. Death":

"I was born wild.
I was almost tamed.
Then I rebelled.
I was exiled.
I searched for truth!
It was unreachable.
I found love.
It was unreliable.
I found beauty.

It was untouchable,
And perishable.
I was lonely.
I wrote a poem.
No one smiled at me.
Except for Mr. Death.
I ran and hid inside his smile."

The next poet is a women with bootcamp hair
And such hatred in her eyes
That Hafez slides down in his chair.
The woman growls her poem the way
German shepherds growl at happy cats.
She calls her poem "The Roles of Holes and Poles":

"The mystery of sex,
In the supermarket of life is this:
There are more holes than poles.
Yet holes are so dear while poles are a dime a dozen.
So biology defies the theory of Supply and Demand,
Night after night."

The audience obediently claps,
And some angry man shouts, "Right-on! Yes!"
The Dull Professor next announces that
A new poet named Pirooz has entered the slam.
So Pirooz takes his poem from his coat and shuffles to the stage,
And nervously adjusts his red beret,
As if it were the volume knob on a radio.
"The name of my poem is Fuzzy Dardedel," he says,
"Written in honor of Lotfi Zadeh, the Iranian scientist,
Who first introduced the concept of fuzzy logic and thought."
He clears his throat and begins:

"Strolling on a foggy night,
Talking to Zadeh, a witty scientist,
I discovered how fuzzy our minds are.
When I told him that my lover wore red silk
He asked me: 'What shade of red?'
I said: 'Well, it was not maroon or magenta or pink,
But a sexy red just a little lighter than the stoplight
That freezes people in their tracks.'
Zadeh insisted that I 'Be precise!'
A little frustrated, I demanded, 'But how?'
'By specifying the frequency of the light," he said.
Timidly, I asked him: 'Even if I had the frequency for you,
Could you really visualize the exact hue?'
'Only if I used a spectral wheel,' he grinned, suggesting
That the next time we met I should bring a scale and tape
To measure words like heavy and short, too.
He smiled the most teasingly fuzzy smile.

"We said goodnight but a pesky question stayed with me:
How can words, paintings, music describe anything precisely?
One can visualize a *dove*, its meaning rather crisp and clear.
But words like love, truth, beauty, happiness, sadness, joy,
Do not project meanings well defined.
These are intoxicated words—fuzzy, fuzzy words,
Meandering human consciousness like crazy hordes,
Making communication as hazardous
As swimming along shark-infested shores.
Even in the austere world of math and logic
Incompleteness, randomness, and fuzziness are rife.
Vagueness permeates everything—even love.

"Reality is infinite and eternal,
But language is finite and temporal.

When the troubled mind complains,
Language shouts back to the mind:
'You created me fuzzy, even inadequate,
And now you complain that I am inadequate?
You remind me of God who creates lemons
But commands them to be persimmons!'

"Even if we are fuzzy from head to toe,
We are still condemned to communicate from head to toe.
So we imprecisely, though efficiently, say what we want to say
And others imprecisely, though efficiently, understand what we say.
Thus this poem of mine is more or less fuzzy.
And more or less fuzzy is fuzzy, too."

The applause is timid and unsure,
Until Rumi jumps up
And slaps his hands together like a maid beating dirty rugs.
Soon everyone is on their feet,
Firecracking with their feet and their hands.
Pirooz, relieved that he is finished, rushes back to the table,
And buries his face in the wide mouth of his cappuccino cup.

"That was very nice," says Hafez, patting him on the back,
"Though I fear you too clearly made your point,
For it to be a truly great poem."
"Nonsense!" Rumi says. "It was perfectly fuzzy!"
"Thank you, Mowlana," Pirooz mumbles.

The next poet is old and bony and his skin
Is as translucent as the hide of a saltwater shrimp.
He screams his poem—"Birthplace/Earthplace"—so loud
And so very fast that the microphone howls in surrender:

"Born into a filthy world I picked up a big broom and

Tried to sweep the big filth away.
But as *I pooshed and pooshed* the broom,
I found my broom and me reflected in a mirror,
Along with the big filthy world I was trying to clean.
Hopeless, enraged, disgusted, afraid,
I threw the broom at the mirror,
Shattering the filthy world,
Shattering my filthy broom and filthy self,
Making the filthy world filthier yet.
So I went home and took a nap."

The slam goes on, poet after poet, poem after poem,
Caffeine empowering the crowd
To cheer, to boo, to clap and stomp,
To demand more and more.
A wayward Catholic priest,
His new wife cheering him on,
Scrambles to the stage and recites the poem
He calls "Holy Material Me":

"I am addicted to oxygen—let me breathe.
I am addicted to sex—let me touch.
I am addicted to food and wine—let me eat and sip.
I am addicted to music—let me tap my foot.
I am addicted to beauty—let me take it in.
I am addicted to life—Let me live.
My think, my feel, and my love exist because matter exists.
Praise be to the Holy Matter, creator of what exists."

Now a Swedish woman takes the stage.
She has a string of carrots around her neck
And a huge flashlight in each hand.
As she recites her poem she
Splashes the ceiling and the walls,

And the stunned faces of the audience,
With Tinker Bell circles of dizzying light.
She calls her poem "New God of the New Eden":
"I rush to visit the New God of the fields,
As the headlines screamingly advertise,
That His Holiness has just arrived
In the Garden of Eden recently modified,
In a biosphere surrounded by barbed-wire and false meaning.

"I find the New God standing upright,
In white robes, smirking, cross-eyed,
Dribbling copper pennies on his chin.
He is nothing but a scientist mad with greed,
Keyed to success by engineering new seeds,
Sanctified by progress to commit bio-misdeeds,
Bio-Frankensteining tomatoes and potatoes,
Bio-Frankensteining lima beans, nature, and man.

"I demand through my bullhorn: 'Why, but why?'

"His Holiness declares: 'Dear child,
This is the process necessary to feed
The *quantity* of wide open mouths
That thoughtless copulation has produced.
I create largesse for those who lack finesse,
The *quantity* which devours the *quality*.

"'So blame me not,'
Sayeth the New God of the New Eden.
'For I am the Father, The Sun God,
And the Holy Short-order Cook.
Take my body, eat, and copulate.'"

Hafez leans toward Pirooz and whispers:

121

"I often recited my poems holding a lighted candle.
I remember once . . ."
Hafez cannot finish his story because
He is suddenly gasping and grabbing at his heart,
Seeing on the stage a beautiful young woman,
Wearing a long dress, as white as any bride's.
He jabs the air with his finger until he can speak:
"Mitra! That is Mitra! My Mitra!"
It is the first time Pirooz has seen her.
He sees immediately why Hafez has fallen.
"My God," he whispers. "If this is Mitra, then who needs God!"
"Yes," Rumi whispers back. "She is both the embodiment of love
And the body of love—in one body."

All three watch with awe as Mitra floats to the microphone,
Folds her delicate hands in front of her young breasts,
And repeats some very old words:

"My beloved is white and ruddy,
The chiefest among ten thousand.
His head is as the most fine gold,
His locks are bushy, and black as a raven.
His eyes are as the eyes of doves by the rivers of waters,
Washed with milk and fitly set.
His cheeks are as a bed of spices, as sweet flowers,
His lips like lilies, dropping sweet smelling myrrh.
His mouth is most sweet, yea, he is altogether lovely.
This is my beloved and this is my friend."

The audience is silent, stunned, perplexed,
Uncertain about what it has heard.
Who is this young woman?
And what were those words?
Those simple, sweet, bodacious words of love?

Where was the required anger?
The sour irony and self-indulgent angst?
The opaque allusions,
The translucent delusions?
The required gloom and doom?

Hafez jumps to his feet and spreads his arms,
And as Mitra walks toward him he offers a poem of his own.
Like hers, it is from the ancient Hebraic love songs,
From an old testament as new as the newest love,
From "The Song of Solomon":

"How beautiful are thy feet with shoes,
O prince's daughter!
The joints of thy thighs are like jewels,
The work of the hands of a cunning workman.
Thy navel is like a round goblet which wanteth not liquor.
Thy belly is like an heap of wheat set about with lilies.
Thy two breasts are like two young roes that are twins.
Thy neck is as a tower of ivory.
Thine eyes like the fishpools in Heshbon,
By the gate of Bathrabbim . . . ."

Now, as the entire audience sits frozen,
Hafez and Mitra walk slowly toward each other,
Their separate voices joining into one voice,
Like lyric and melody dovetailing.
Together they finish the verses that Hafez had begun:

"Come, my beloved,
Let us go forth into the field.
Let us lodge in the villages.
Let us get up early to the vineyards.
Let us see if the grapes flourish,

Whether the tender grape appear,
And the pomegranates bud forth.
There I will give thee my loves."

There is no silence now.
There is no uncertainty or perplexment.
There is only long and tender applause,
The sour poets of Manhattan tamed at last.

"Mitra! I am so surprised!" sings Hafez to Mitra,
As he leads her to their table by the kitchen door.
"Your mother said you couldn't come with me,
Yet here you are! How is this, Mitra Jaan?"
Mitra shrugs and smiles:
"She said I couldn't come to the slam with you,
But she didn't say I couldn't come to the slam with me."
Hafez cocks his head suspiciously, the way wise roosters do.
"Mitra Jaan, I wasn't born yesterday.
Tell me the truth, did you sneak out?"
Again Mitra shrugs: "How can I sneak out,
If my mother is not home to catch me?
If she is away on one of her business trips,
Minding other people's business,
And not the business of her own child?"
"That sounds like sneaking out to me," Rumi says flatly.
Mitra is worried: "You aren't going to tell my mother, are you?"

Rumi erases her fear with a grandfatherly laugh.
"We will not tell your mother about your disobedience,
If you don't tell our mothers about ours!"
Only Pirooz does not laugh at this.
His stomach is bubbling with concern.
Mitra is clearly a fantastic girl,
But she is still a girl,

124

And Hafez, even in his present incarnation,
Is a grown man, with a growing problem,
Should he take his love for the girl too far.
"Do your friends have names?" Mitra asks Hafez.
Not wanting to give away his own secret,
Hafez introduces Rumi simply as Jalalad-Din,
"A good poet who knows the works of Rumi
As if he wrote them himself—and this is Professor Pirooz,
Who read an excellent poem about our fuzzy world,
Just before you arrived."

The Dull Professor now introduces a poet
Who rode on a train all the way from Ohio.
Hafez, studying the poet's face and beret,
Is both amused and astonished:
"Pirooz, give or take a few gray hairs, that man could be you!"

Pirooz's eyes and mind drift from Mitra.
He immediately nods and immediately frowns.
"Yes, yes, that is Manoucher,
A Persian like us, and a scholar like me.
He taught at Columbia when I first came,
And despite my best efforts people were forever mixing us up.
He is something of an imp, I'm afraid.
I can't tell you how many times his antics were blamed on me,
And my good work credited to him!"

As the poet from Ohio takes the stage, a bird alights on his arm.
Pirooz whispers, "Look there!
It is the Poem of Poems, sitting there proudly,
Just like a pirate's parrot!
Do you think anyone sees him but us?"
"Does anyone see what?" Mitra wonders.
"There is your answer," Mowlana whispers back to Pirooz.

"Now everyone listen to the poet and forget his muse."

Manoucher's voice rises slowly and softly,
Like the fresh Caspian breezes of his youth.
His poem is entitled, "Where Have All the Directions Gone?":

"Oh, how easy it is to desire truth and
Journey on and on to seek it.
But navigation is difficult if the path is uncharted and
Your destination unknown.
Navigation is the orchestration of space, of time, of things,
Of imaginations and intentions,
A struggle to uproot familiarities,
To know the unknown and see the unseen.
Navigation says no to traditions, no to boundaries, no to fate.
No, no, no to fate!

"We each choose different routes,
Even to reach the same destination.
We mark the North Star,
We invent compasses, maps, signs, chronometers, and radar.
We number buildings, name streets.
Still we ask for directions,
Whether we are lost or not,
And we wonder how to navigate and where to navigate,
Within the jungle of our thoughts
And the cravings of our hearts,
Where both destination and direction remain:
Anonymous, enigmatic, indeterminate, and unresolved.
We must navigate alone to inadmissible futures,
Without signs, guides, landmarks, or wisdom provided,
By our genes, or the gods, or the magic of our times.

"I know that my destination

Is not a garden of artificial flowers,
Is not a graveyard of unfulfilled goals,
Is not a heaven or a hell or a purgatory
Silenced of all earthly senses or truths.
My destination is not death or after death.
My destination is now, is life itself.
My destination is the heart and mind of Mankind.

"I live with the hope that man will navigate to where love is not sin,
To where shame is gone, where fear is dead,
Where injustice is abolished and jealously self-devoured,
Where peace is a grinning rose on War's deep grave
Where happiness sails everywhere with the power of a wish."

The Dull Professor makes a last call for poets,
Before the judges judge,
And the waitresses stack the chairs.
"Go on, Jalalad-Din," Hafez urges Rumi,
"Everyone here has slammed but you!"
"Yes, please, Jalalad-Din," begs Pirooz,
"Consummate your marriage to the modern world,
And like the virgin bride you are,
Wear something old and something new,
Something borrowed and something blue!"
Rumi drums his fingers on the table,
Then says, "Well, well, why not!"
He bumps back his chair and hurries to the stage.
But when he arrives, he is not the white-bearded Persian he was,
But a young man, even younger than Hafez,
His new face wearing every ethnicity,
Crowned with a baseball cap turned backwards,
Cloaked in great baggy jeans and a shirt to his knees.

"What happened to Jalalad-Din?" asks Mitra,

Trying to find him in the dark, crowded room.
"Perhaps he has lost his way," says Hafez quickly.
"Or his mind," worries a quivering Pirooz.
They listen to the young rapper,
His body and his words bobbing rhythmically:

"Just maxin' and relaxin'
Kickin' my ballistics
Rappin' realistic
Hip-hoppin'
Ain't stoppin'
Hangin' in my garden
Flowers stickin' through the concrete
Tickling at my phat feet
While I'm whirlin'
And I'm twirling
While I'm doin' the Sama
The deep-down cosmic dance
That the Dervishes do in their pajamas.

"Don't dis me
Don't dismiss me
Cause I ain't comin' off
Just to hear myself talk.
Can't you see I'm ascending?
Can't you see I'm transcending?
My flesh and my bones
Moving to a new home
To the Big MC's
Kingdom of Wisdom
To the fly-far-away world
Of rhyme and reason
To the garden of raps
Where Jesus and Buddha

Moses and the Dali Lama
Are doin' the Sama
The deep-down cosmic dance
That the Dervishes do in their pajamas."

BOOK THREE:

Love of All Loves

11 West Side Stories, East Side Stories

The sun-sprinkled rain drips off the curbs, trickles into the streets,
Hums into the treads of spinning tires,
Soaks into the leather soles of fashionable shoes.
It is summer again.

All winter, all spring, Hafez drove Mitra home,
And each day told her how much he loved her:
During their stolen moments in Central Park,
While holding hands in the city's quiet museums,
While holding each other inside the telephone's mystical wires
Where longings travel beyond the reach of eyes or fingertips.
Yet while he opened his heart to her,
Saying to her so many times, "Mitra Jaan, I die for you,"
He still could not tell her the truth about himself,
That he is not only a young cabbie named Hafez,
That this is not his first bumpy ride through mortal life,
That he is the real Hafez, the poet Hafez,
The Hafez who lived and who died centuries ago,
Before there was a New York City,
Before there were yellow automobiles with magic meters
That could spin time and space into gold,
Before there was a young woman with
Intermingling Persian and American blood,
Named Mitra.

Hafez knows he must tell her the truth, and soon,
Lest their lovers' dardedel be false and hollow.
Each day he reminds himself, "Today I will tell her my secret."
Yet each day passes with the secret left a secret.

131

Each day he warns himself that, "She will fear you,
Run from you, hide from you, and curse you for your deceit."

But now it is summer, and all things are possible in summer,
When temperatures rise, flowers open, and fruits ripen irresistibly.
So he will tell her today, perhaps,
And let his truth test the truth of their love.
Perhaps today, perhaps tomorrow.

Today is a Saturday, the Saturday after the Saturday that
Mitra, wearing her white gown and funny flat hat, graduated.
She had wept and wept, not in joy, but in sadness,
Because her father was too far away to attend.
But the week has fled and the tears have dried,
And now Mitra asks Hafez to meet her at Times Square.
"I have a secret for you," she says on the phone.
Hafez races in his cab, hoping her secret is no worse than his,
That she will not confess that she is not really Mitra,
But the incarnated beguiling god of light,
Who long ago slew the sacred bull and gave life to life,
And now comes to New York to toy with love.

Mitra spots him and jumps into the front seat of his cab, saying,
"I have tickets, Hafez Jaan! Tickets!"
"And so do I," laments Hafez, popping his glove compartment.
"Speeding tickets and parking tickets,
Tickets for making U's and tickets for going the wrong way,
More tickets than I can begin to pay!"
"My tickets are free," Mitra says,
"A gift of guilt from my mother for being on business
When she should be here for my birthday.
One of my parents is always missing on special days.
They take turns disappointing me, then shower me with gifts.
It is a lucrative but lonely life I live, Hafez Jaan."

"Today is your birthday? You should have told me, Mitra Jaan!
I would have brought you a present!"
Mitra grins with a trace of wicked enjoyment at the tips of her lips.
"I hope my being fifteen doesn't drive you to a younger woman!"
Hafez grins back, feeling as guilty as her parents.
What would she think of him if she knew the truth—
That he is not just five years older than her, but six hundred?
"What are the tickets for?" he finally asks.
"For a play!" she says, "A wonderful play
With wonderful music and dancing!
My mother said I should take a friend from school,
And what better friend do I have *from* school than you?"
She hugs him, and burns a hole in his cheek with a quick kiss.
"So we have all day together, and all night if you wish."
(The words "all night" send a worldly trembling through Hafez,
One he has not felt for a long, long time.)

Hafez calms himself and parks his cab and they run
To the marquee that reads: WEST SIDE STORY.
"It is an old play," Mitra tells him as they shuffle into line,
"But so good they keep bringing it back."
Whispers Hafez: "It is good that good things from the past
Are allowed now and then to visit the future."
Three hours later they are in a coffee shop, chewing on fresh bagels,
Sipping fruit juice through plastic straws.
As they talk of the impossible love between Tony and Maria,
Neither can keep the tears from their eyes.
"This Bernstein and Sondheim," says Hafez of the play's authors,
"Were great seers to write our story before there was us!
Who are Tony and Maria but Mitra and Hafez?"
Mitra wants to cry—But she giggles instead.
"Actually Tony and Maria are two Italians named Romeo and Juliet,
Created by an Englishman named Shakespeare, centuries ago."
She tells him of Shakespeare's famous play,

133

Of the star-crossed lovers who ended as Tony and Maria ended,
Because hatred engulfed their families.
"How is it you have never heard of Romeo and Juliet?" she wonders
As the sweet juice gurgles up the plastic straw
Into the pucker between her pink lips.
Hafez, of course, has never heard of Romeo or Juliet,
Or this Shakespeare or this Sondheim or this Bernstein.
For the longest time he was a wandering soul in Heaven,
And then a star-counting cactus in the desert.
But he cannot tell Mitra that—that truth is trapped in his secret,
The secret he must tell, but cannot tell.
Instead he says: "Actually, Tony and Maria are not Romeo and Juliet.
They are two lovers named—"
Angry tears erupt in Mitra's eyes. "You have already reminded me
That they are the doomed lovers named Mitra and Hafez!"
Hafez almost shouts at her:
"No, Mitra! They are not us! We will never be them!"
His voice softens and he takes her hand.
"I am speaking of two lovers named Layla and Majnun!
How is it that you have never heard of them,
When you can recite Hafez and Rumi as if
You had once studied at their knees?"

"I may be graduating three years early," she teases,
"But I am only fifteen years old, and only half Persian.
Tell me about them, Hafez Jaan."
And so Hafez does: "The story of Layla and Majnun is very old,
So old that perhaps Adam and Eve themselves,
The most famous star-crossed lovers of all time,
Heard it from a bluebird in the garden of Eden.
But the version Persians love most
Was written eight hundred years ago by the poet Nizami,
When Islam was in full flower, fertilized by Persia's rich loam.
Nizami wrote Layla and Majnun at the urging

Of his patron, Sharvan Shah Akhsitan Manuchehr,
Who wanted a new retelling of the story.
Nizami was reluctant—it was already so famous a tale—
But the shah insisted and so Nizami wrote!
Mitra Jaan! What a poet was Nizami!
His invention and imagery are still without equal."
"Even better than the poems of Hafez?" asks Mitra.
Without a blush, Hafez answers:
"Hafez could not hold a candle to him,
Though Hafez wished he had lived in Nizami's time,
So he could have stood behind him with a candle,
And studied the great master as he worked."
"Enough of Nizami," says Mitra. "Tell me the story Nizami wrote."

And so Hafez begins the story of Layla and Majnun:
"There once lived in the desert of Arabia a wealthy chieftain,
Loved for his goodness and wisdom.
He prayed to God for a son and was given one,
A handsome boy whom he named Qays.
Qays was sent to the finest school, where he did his father proud,
His future looked very bright.
But then another chieftain sent his daughter to the same school.
Layla was her name and she was very beautiful,
As slender as a cypress tree, as graceful as a bird,
Possessing raven hair and the darting black eyes of a gazelle.
She looked just like you, Mitra Jaan.
Except for your blue eyes, of course!
Anyway, Qays immediately fell in love with her.
And Layla fell immediately in love with him.
Even at his tender age Qays claimed her for his own
And vowed he would love her all his life.
Poor Qays! His heart and mind were so filled with love
That he could do nothing but think of Layla.
When he opened his mouth, only Layla's name came out.

You think Tony had it bad for Maria?
You think Romeo had it bad for Juliet?
Qays had it as bad for Layla as I have it bad for you, Mitra Jaan!
That is how bad!"

"Since Qays was madly in love, he became insane with love!
When Qays ran through the bazaar calling, 'Layla! Layla!'
People said, 'Indeed he is a madman, a Majnun!'
And so Qays came to be known as Majnun.
When word of Majnun's mad love reached Layla's father,
He withdrew her from the school, to protect her.
Without Layla, Majnun lost his senses completely and
Wandered into the wilderness where his madness only grew.
I know just what Majnun was going through, Mitra Jaan,
Just what Romeo and Tony went through.
When you are in the back seat of my cab,
So close and yet so far from my reach,
I am Majnun in the wilderness, Majnun in New York.
As he sang Layla's name across the sands, I sing for you, Mitra!"

Hafez now begins to sing the lines Tony's sang to Maria:
"The most beautiful sound I've ever heard:
Mitra, Mitra, Mitra, Mitra . . .
All the beautiful sounds of the world in a single word:
Mitra, Mitra, Mitra, Mitra . . .
Say it loud and it's music playing,
Say it soft and it's almost like praying . . ."
Mitra squeezes Hafez's hand to stop him.
"Hafez Jaan, please! The girl making bagels is laughing at you."
Hafez turns toward the bagel girl and blows her a kiss,
Then continues his story: "Yes, Majnun went completely mad,
And his father, his heart breaking, too,
Went to Layla's father to ask for her hand.
But Layla's father refused to give Layla to Majnun,

136

And so Majnun wandered deeper into the wilderness,
Deeper into his madness.
I do not know why Romeo could not have Juliet,
And it seems so foreign to me that Tony and Maria
Were denied simply because one was white and one brown,
But how tragic it was that Majnun could not have Layla,
Simply because he loved her too much!"

Mitra tells him quickly of Romeo and Juliet's plight:
"Romeo was a Montague and Juliet a Capulet,
Two families that hated each other.
Their love was doomed from the start—
But tell me more about Layla: did she go as mad as Majnun?"
Hafez shrugs, answering: "She did not go mad,
Though she was madly in love with Majnun.
When her father forced her to marry another man,
She refused her husband's bed,
And just as Majnun spent his life wandering the wilderness,
Layla was lost in a wilderness, too, in a cold and loveless marriage."

Mitra is holding Hafez's hands tight.
She asks, not wanting to know the answer,
"How did it end for Layla and Majnun?"
"They lived long and empty lives," says Hafez,
"Always apart, yet always in love.
When Layla died, Majnun rushed to her grave,
And wept until he, too, died.
His bones were buried with Layla's bones—a vasal in death."

"Romeo and Juliet died in each other's arms," Mitra says.
"How do you think we will fare?"
Hafez searches for an answer, finding only his own misery.
"I do not want to live and die as Majnun lived and died,
I do not want to live and die as Romeo or Tony lived and died.

I want you now, in life, right now!
But the law says *no* because you are too young,
That loving you is rape, though you are already ripe,
And as willing as I am willing.
The law is the rapist, Mitra Jaan!
It is the crazy modern laws of crazy modern men
That are the defilers and deflowerers!
Once our love would have been blessed by God and our families,
Once the mullahs would have whirled in their robes with joy for us!"

Hafez is now Majnun, by madness transformed into an empty desert.
"And what is wrong with your mother, Mitra Jaan?
That she does not want love for you?
That she does not see that you are a grown woman?
That she bribes you with free tickets to plays
That will only fuel your longings and your agony?"
Mitra is crying: "It is more than the crazy laws,
More than my age or your age that divides us.
It is more than you are a cabbie and a lover of poems.
You are a Persian, Hafez, an Iranian, like my father.
And while my mother loves all things Persian,
She no longer loves the Persian who fathered me."
Hafez laughs as he cries, lamenting:
"So we must carry the burden of all star-crossed lovers!
Like Majnun and Romeo, Layla and Juliet,
We are kept apart by family pride.
Like Tony and Maria we are kept apart by color and culture.
And on top of everything, we are kept apart by modern laws
That make a mockery of nature's design,
That seek to stop our biological clocks, as Pirooz calls them,
That tell men and women ready for love they are not ready for love!
As you and I are ready for love! Mitra! I am ready for love!"
Says Mitra: "And I am ready for love."

Hafez is now quivering with gloom and shame,
For he has not confessed the other thing keeping them apart:
That he is the old poet Hafez, on a vacation granted by God,
That instead of the cactus counting stars he is again a living man,
A young man in love with a young woman,
Wanting no longer to count stars, but make love under them,
As if he had never died and his flesh never rotted in his grave,
As if this city were not New York but Shiraz.
He sits there, now, squeezing Mitra's hands,
Begging his tongue to tell her the truth now,
Now and now and now,
In the hope that she will say, "Hafez Jaan,
It is okay that you have kept this secret from me,
Okay that God at any second may snap you away.
For, Hafez, I love you as Layla loves Majnun,
As Juliet loves Romeo, as Maria loves Tony,
As my mother once loved my father, as Eve once loved Adam,
As poets love words, as Love loves all lovers."
But Hafez's tongue will not budge and
His secret remains a monster.

They walk hand in hand to Hafez's cab.
Already the sidewalks are crowded
With people arriving for the evening shows.
Hafez removes the parking ticket from his windshield,
Shrugs the shrug of a modern man and drives Mitra home.
"Come in for a while," Mitra pleads. "The place is so big and lonely."
The elevator ascends to a safe and expensive world above the streets.
The apartment *is* big and it *is* lonely.
It also is too clean and too tidy, the furniture and rugs too new.
They sit like careful butterflies on the white leather sofa
And smile at each other, a silent dardedel.
Finally Mitra asks: "Would you like some wine, Hafez?

To help us say the things we want to say?"
He nods.

She brings two delicate goblets of delicate white wine.
He sips and watches her sip.
"Does your mother approve of wine for you, Mitra Jaan?"
She watches him sip.
"If my mother were here, she would not be worried
About me drinking wine—She would be worried
About the way your eyes are drinking me,
And the way my eyes are drinking you."

They sip in silence, allowing their eyes
To devour as they wish, all they wish.
Whispers Hafez: "Sweet Mitra Jaan!
I can't take my eyes off your alluring eyes,
Or your supple lips, or seducing hair,
Or your curvatures—oh, yes, your curvatures—
And your torturing walk as you glide about with that
Silky teasing skirt pouring excited bees into my empty hive,
Revealing more or revealing less, saying yes then saying no,
As you swing around to pick up this or pick up that,
Or just sitting across from me with your naked thighs
Resting on the soft leather, making me jealous of the soft leather,
That was once a beast and now touches you ravenously,
Without shame or pity for my tortured eyes to see!"

Mitra feels her wine glass trembling against her aching lips.
"Hafez Jaan, say no more, or I will have to torture you more."
Hafez reaches for the wine bottle, to refill his glass.
But Mitra reaches it before him and slides it away,
As a lover pulls her lips away to make the next kiss more enjoyable.
"Mitra, Please! I am still thirsty!"
Mitra laughs mischievously, filling his ears with erotic sensations.

"I think God first created thirst, then everything else for the thirst!
Don't blame me, Hafez, I am thirsty, too—
But don't ask me for what!"

Now Mitra lifts the bottle,
As if it were made of fragile morning dew.
"Drink another drink, Hafez, to quench your thirst,
The thirst of thirsts."
She stands to fill his glass and glances into his eyes,
To see how they glance back at her.
Then she twirls around, a merry-go-round of silk and silken skin.
"I can see that you like my skirt more up than more down."
Hafez can barely hold his glass still.
"Why not bring a sword and slice me in half, Mitra Jaan?"
"Patience, my love," she says. "I will do that later—perhaps."

Though he wants to sip the new wine,
Hafez must put his glass down on the table,
For the moment of truth has come.
"My beloved, my goddess," he says,
"Will you hear my confession before you cut me down?"
Mitra enjoys being called a goddess,
And smiles a goddess's smile.
"What possibly does a mortal man have to confess,
That a goddess does not already know?"

Hafez steadies his knees and finds the breath he needs.
"Mitra, you will not believe me, but you must believe me,
For the unbelievable is the truth.
I am the real Hafez, Hafez of Shiraz, the old and dead Hafez,
An unholy spirit, a poet trying to live as long as his poems!"
Mitra reaches and caresses Hafez's thick hair with her fingers,
As if they were the delicate ivory teeth of a goddess's comb.
"I know you are the real Hafez, Hafez.

141

I feel it in my bones and in my heart."
"You do?"
"Yes. For a long time."
"You have?"
"And suspected it even longer."
"But how?"
Mitra shrugs shyly, admitting, "At first it was just a notion,
Then it grew so strong that I felt it must be true.
Then that night at the slam, at the Sad Ghazal,
You introduced me to your friend, Jalalad-Din.
'A very good poet who knows the works of Rumi
As if he wrote them himself,' you said.
This is New York, but not Disneyland, Hafez!
What are the odds that a cabbie named Hafez,
Who knows the work of the poet Hafez as well as Hafez,
Has a friend with Rumi's name
Who knows the poems of Rumi as well as Rumi?
I had no doubt after that:
Hafez is Hafez and Rumi is Rumi.
The only thing that puzzled me was Pirooz—who was he really?"

Hafez is scratching his head now.
"As far as I can tell, Pirooz is really Pirooz.
Mitra! Why didn't you tell me you knew?
You don't know how many nights of sleep this secret has cost me,
How many bottles of wine this secret has cost me!"
And so the secret is no longer a secret.
They laugh and laugh, each laugh easier than the last.
Hafez now says this: "Mitra Jaan, my love is not just
The love of one soul for another,
But the love of one body for another."
"Tell me something new," teases Mitra, still playing the goddess.
"I never believed your poems were all mystical as some fools do!
Mystical love is for mystical birds nesting in mystical trees,

142

And I always saw real birds in real trees when reading your poems.
Now go on with your confession, Hafez Jaan."

Hafez obeys: "Night after night I'm on fire
Burning for you, to kiss you, to be annihilated inside you.
No one, and nothing, will stop me,
Not in this life.
My new life belongs to no one but you and me,
Not the national religion that Pirooz curses,
Not your mother who disapproves of me,
Not kings! Not angels! Not even God!

"If you desire fire, touch me, Mitra Jaan.
Let me burn with you, in male and female flames,
The flames of vasal, union, and fruition, Mitra Jaan.
And let me disappear in your palpitations,
And turn into dust and be blown away,
To immortal joy, by your palpitations."

Mitra walks slowly to Hafez, and stands just an inch away from him,
A curious moth unable to resist a dancing flame.
Hafez rests his head on her drumming heart, looks up, and whispers:
"I have waited centuries for you.
I will wait for you no longer.
I want to be wrong, so very wrong.
Let us do something wrong, Mitra,
And never, never apologize,
For this single *wrong* that is better than all rights.
And if the cloaked men say repent, we will pretend we are deaf.
And if the laws declare you too young,
Those laws will be the footprints of a thousand confused birds to us.
And if people say we are worlds apart, like America and Iran,
We will orbit both worlds like a pair of illuminating moons."
Hafez stands and holds Mitra gently,

Her hair carressing his cheek like a soft pillow.
"Mitra Jaan! Give me permission to awaken and ignite your passion.
For surely God knows we're destined to be reborn in each other's fire."
Mitra feels ablaze, like Zoroaster's eternal flame.
"Stop Hafez! My inside has been aching for your passion, too,
Through your poems, even before your resurrection!"

Hafez is shocked to learn about such passion for his poems,
But he has another kind of poetry on his mind:
"Mitra Jaan, I am not mad, I am not Majnun,
Destined just to write poems in the wilderness,
And give them up to the winds,
In the hope the winds will carry them to Layla.
No, I am not Majnun, destined to go mad and stay mad,
To wander over rock and sand, to live in caves and talk to animals.
I just left the desert for New York, Mitra Jaan!
I am in the fertile jungle of love now,
In the home of my love now.
Majnun persisted in his madness for many years,
But over the years of separation Layla had become
Only an image, an impossible dream.
And when she died, widowed, but yet untouched,
Majnun wept over her grave, but this was the grave of a dream.
I am mad for you, Mitra Jaan!
You are my dream, Mitra Jaan!
You are my goddess, in the daylight and in the moonlight.
With every breath I declare to you:
I will never leave you and your love will never leave me.
Our love story won't repeat that of Layla and Majnun,
Romeo and Juliet, Tony and Maria,
All the tragic loves of all places and times.

"God has not reincarnated me to let tragedy pounce on me,
Not to deprive us of our vasal, Mitra Jaan.

We are here to avenge all the unfulfilled loves.
Our love is the Almighty's apology to mankind.
Our love is the Almighty's apology to love.
I am certain of it!"

Hafez caresses Mitra's glowing neck,
Then lets his fingers find her breasts.
"Mitra Jaan, I am a Mitraist!
Even in ancient times when I was as young as I am now
I worshipped Mitra.
And even after my death some people persist I am a Mitraist."
And I am! Indeed I am!"
Mitra puts her hands on his hands for the longest moment
And then reluctantly draws them away.
There is both sadness and sweetness in her voice.
"Sorry Hafez, I love you but our vasal will have to wait."
She stands and pulls him up.
But instead of walking him to the door,
She walks him down a hallway, to a bedroom
Set aside by her absent mother for guests who never visit.
"Rest here, my love, and in the morning I'll fix you breakfast.
And then you will flee before my mother comes home."
She kisses his cheek and leaves quickly.
Hafez throws himself on the bed and weeps and weeps,
Such rivers of tears that even Majnun and Layla
Together could not weep.

12 Angels Listening at the Door

Hafez tries to sleep but he is kept awake by crushing thoughts,
Tumbling and bouncing through his hollow mind.
Why is he not in Mitra's arms? Why is he not in Mitra's arms?
It is not a family feud that keeps them apart tonight,
Not ethnic differences or religious differences,
Not ignorance or his station in life,
Not mothers, not Rumi, not Pirooz,
Not modern laws, not ancient gods.
Nor is it his own secret, the secret that was no secret to Mitra at all.
No, Hafez concludes, it is Mitra herself that keeps them apart.
Mitra, the lovely and delicate stone wall that
Stands between them and their vasal.
How unbearably noisy it is inside his hollow mind.

Was Mitra, this goddess of light and kindness,
Resurrected to reject the resurrected Hafez,
A terrible cosmic joke played by the Creator
Upon this ghost of a man?
Why was she eagerly saying yes until the moment she said no?
Is Pirooz correct?
Is she but a child, ready but not ready?
Layla, Juliet, Maria never said no.
Yet it is true that their *yesses*, and the fires they ignited,
Created the ashes of their tragedy.
Maybe Mitra is not wicked, or afraid, but merely wise,
As wise as he should be wise!

Hafez almost flees home to Pirooz's apartment,
To drink whiskey and watch TV and forget;

146

Almost flees home to the Sonora to resume counting stars;
Almost flees home to Heaven to resume his eternal retirement;
But as he ponders the destination of his flight,
Rumi's words come to him:

"When disappointed, I become encouraged.
When in pain, I breathe easier.
When I am ruined, I heal myself."

And so Hafez whispers to himself:
"No matter how painful my misadventure becomes,
I could never leave Mitra!"
Now he begins to weep again, weep and weep.
He weeps for star-crossed lovers everywhere,
And for the lovers of one-sided loves, the most-difficult loves.
He weeps until his eyes are desert dry and desert red,
Until in his dreams he is a bull felled on the ground,
And Mitra is the god Mitra, her hands wielding a dreadful sword,
A curled Persian scimitar,
Wondering aloud whether to strike or not to strike.
His voice, now the voice of fate, screams to her:
"Strike at me, strike me in the heart, my blood will be the creation!"

Resolved, Mitra plunges the scimitar into his heart.
Blood spurting from his bull's chest splashes the pearly ground
And forms into one of his own poems,
In his own hand, in the reddest of indelible inks:

Her lips dewy and her curls tangled
Drunk, giggling and singing,
Her blouse ajar—holding a jug of wine,
Her narcissus eyes sparkling and her lips alluring,
She slipped into my bed last night at midnight,
And brought her lips to my ear and whispered soulfully:

"Are you awake my grieved old lover?"

Horrified and bewildered, Hafez awakes to a black room and
Mitra's melodic voice sliding through the cracks of the closed door.
Her words are also his words:
"Are you awake my grieved old lover?"

Not knowing if he is still awake or still asleep,
In the desert or in heaven,
Hafez rubs his eyes and then digs his fingernails
Into the fleshy end of his nose to illicit a telling pang of pain.
He is awake.
Now the door opens and Mitra enters,
Not with a scimitar but with a jug of wine.
The wine inside the jug is the same red
As the ballerina's leotard that hugs her tight.
She sits on the bed and touches his chin.
"So Hafez Jaan—are you awake or aren't you?"
Answers Hafez: "Dead or alive I have never been so awake."
He reaches and gently combs her tangled curls,
And wipes the invisible dew from her lips.
And now, with Mitra's smile in his eyes,
And with Mitra's hand over his hand,
He softly touches her eyes, her nose, her chin and cheeks,
Her neck and breasts, her stomach and hips,
Her knees and her thighs, every inch of her,
The way a rolling breeze touches every curvaceous inch
Of the warm, firm and ready earth.
Hafez—Mitraist of old, Mitraist of new—quivers as he sighs,
Knowing now that the ideal lover of Hafez's poems
Is now the real lover of Hafez the man.

Mitra quivers as he quivers, and sighs as he sighs,
Knowing now that she is not only the lover of Hafez's poems,

But also the lover of Hafez the man.
She pushes him into his pillow and
Erecting a silken tent around his face with her hair,
Kisses him gently and long, as if he were a rose or a love poem.
Then with the intensity of a fresh raw fire,
She munches the poet and the poems at once.
Hafez draws her on top of him, his strong arms surrounding her.
He kisses her as she kissed him.

The thirsty lovers drink and drink and drink and drink,
Kissing all the kisses never kissed,
Sacrificing themselves with pleasure,
The way martyrs sacrifice themselves with pain,
For all the loves and lovers never fulfilled.
When finally their lips withdraw,
And they make up for the breaths they forgot,
Hafez laughs softly with the purest of joy.
And he sings the song that burned
Into his ears that afternoon in the theater:
"Tonight, tonight, it all began tonight,
I saw you and the world went away . . ."

They are the only lines Hafez remembers,
But Mitra remembers them all,
For she has visited the song, like Hafez's poems,
Many, many times when alone so many times:
"Today, all day I had the feeling a miracle would happen,
I know now I was right . . ."

Mitra sings and Hafez's hands explore.
He whispers desperately: "For the sake of God, Mitra,
This red skin you are in—this whatever it is!
There are no buttons anywhere, no laces or snaps!
How did you get it on so that I may get it off?"

Answers Mitra: "I know how to put it on, Hafez Jaan,
And I know where and when and for whom to take it off.
Be patient, my love, be patient."
To which Hafez says: "I know I deserve to be tortured,
But this much torture is too much torture!
Do you wish me to be dead again, Mitra Jaan?"
"I don't torture you to make you dead again," she says,
"But to make you more than alive."
Now she stands up and helps him stand up,
And guides him into the living room,
And sits him on the white leather couch.
"I am going to dance for you," she says, retreating to the stereo.
"Stravinsky's Firebird—have you heard of it?"
Hafez shakes his head: "Not unless this Stravinsky is an old Persian,
Or an old coyote in the desert, Mitra Jaan."
She laughs, confidently, womanly,
And readies herself on the moonlit oak floor.
As she begins dancing to the pianissimo rumble,
She tells the story of the Firebird to Hafez:

"Once there was a monster, the most evil monster ever,
Who never died, who turned men into stone,
Who bound women with chains, just for the fun of it.
Under his rule lovers were thus kept apart forever.

"A wandering prince, lost deep in the monster's domain,
Serendipitously encounters a beautiful Firebird.
Struck by the bird's loveliness, he steals a feather.

"The monster captures the prince.
But before the monster can turn him into stone,
And separate him forever from the maiden he loves,
The prince waves the magic feather of the Firebird.
The bird comes to him and helps him escape,

150

And tells him where to find the ogre's secret of immortality—
An egg hidden inside a coffin.

"The prince flees, finds the coffin and smashes the egg,
Killing the monster and freeing its captives.
The evil cast over the land dissolves,
And the men of stone are turned back into men of flesh,
And the women are freed from their chains,
And happiness becomes a curious breeze,
And love flows into every heart."

As Mitra finishes her story and her dance,
The thunderous musical jubilation impels her to leap like a bird.
Her swirling hair, playing peek-a-boo with her sensuous eyes,
Bewitches Hafez, but Hafez does not turn to stone.
He becomes as light and liquid as a bird himself,
And leaps from the sofa, and whirls as the Dervishes do,
And finishes in the arms of Mitra.
The dance, as Mitra intended,
Frees the two lovers from all prohibitions, and all inhibitions,
From the many monsters that had kept them apart,
That had kept them from their lovers' dardedel.
If the jealous world would not give them permission to love,
Then they would take the world into their own hands.

Mitra slips from her leotard.
The earth, even the stars, tremble with delight.
She guides the suddenly shy Hafez to her bedroom,
Where a dozen white candles are already dancing,
Tossing sweet scents as if they were bridesmaids
Scattering the perfumed petals of roses.
She closes the door behind them,
Not to keep the world out, but to keep their love in.
Like a mother, she helps him to undress.

151

The naked virgin lovers stand at the foot of the virgin bed,
Catching their beautiful blushing bodies in a shy virgin mirror.
The mirror blushes back at them,
Filling their eager eyes with their own happy smiles.

The angels of love pour down from heaven and
Gather outside the bedroom door,
And press their ears against the door,
And listen as Hafez and Mitra pray together:
"You are my God, my supreme God,
You are my love, my supreme love,
You are my God, the supreme love,
You are my love, the supreme God."
They hear Hafez and Mitra cry together, laugh together,
Hear their bodies struggling to become one,
Hear their screams of delight,
Hear their screams of accomplishment, their silence,
As they are lifted skyward on the powerful wings of their vasal.

The angels also cry, and also laugh, and also scream with joy,
And later as the spent lovers are touring the Universe,
They dance to the music of the "Rites of Spring,"
Hearing at long last these words:
"You are my perfect lover, Mitra Jaan."
"And you are my perfect lover, Hafez Jaan."
And then Mitra and Hafez hear the angels chanting:
"Happy vasal, happy vasal, happy vasal."

Too soon morning brightens the room and awakens the lovers.
They untangle, shower together, and dress,
And go to the kitchen for breakfast.
This is not a morning for cold cereal!
Hafez makes orange juice from real oranges,

While Mitra scrambles eggs and toasts pita in the oven.
"What now?" Mitra asks as she lights a candle.

It is hard for Hafez to eat eggs
And fondle Mitra's face at the same time—but he is trying.
"What now about the rest of today," he asks,
"Or what now about the rest of our lives?"
"About the rest of our lives, Hafez Jaan."
Hafez doesn't want to shrug—to show Mitra he has no answers—
But what can he do but shrug?
"I suppose we must begin the rest of our lives
Right after we finish the rest of our breakfast.
I will hurry out before your mother hurries in,
So she will never know what we did,
So that when we get a chance we can do it again."
Mitra does not like his answer at all.
"So instead of lovers we will be sneakers?
A pair of running shoes, lost miles apart?
Hafez Jaan! I don't want us to be sneakers!
Romeo and Juliet were sneakers.
And Romeo and Juliet were failures."

Answers Hafez: "We will be sneakers like them
But we will not fail like them!
Because unlike them, we already know their story."
Mitra is not persuaded: "We will sneak and sneak,
Until we are caught, and then just like their story,
Our story will end on a stage slick with tears,
With a curtain of iron inevitability drawn between us."
The eggs and the toast are suddenly too cold to eat.
Hafez catches his falling face in his hands, saying:
"You are right, Mitra Jaan,
We *are* just like them."

Mitra strokes his hair.
"You give up quickly for a man who defies death.
Perhaps we should analyze our plight,
Not like sad, star-crossed lovers, but like scientists,
Postulating theories and then either proving them true,
Or poking them full of holes."
Says Hafez: "If we are to be scientists, Mitra Jaan,
Then perhaps we should recruit Pirooz.
There is nothing he likes better than poking holes
In other people's truths.
And perhaps we should include Rumi, too.
He is as wise as Socrates."
Answers Mitra: "Let Rumi and Pirooz debate the existence of God.
Whether Mitra and Hafez are a complete pair of shoes,
And not just one shoe over here and one over there,
We will handle ourselves."

And so instead of making love they go to Central Park,
Taking the bench they have claimed as their own.
Like scientists they ponder this question:
What common thing was it that doomed the other lovers?

Hafez begins: "Majnun was overwhelmed by his love for Layla,
Driven to madness by it.
Layla spent her entire life waiting in her tent
Hoping he would love her a little less,
So her father would find him more acceptable.
With Romeo and Juliet it was not a matter
Of too much love between them,
But a matter of too much hate between their families.
With Tony and Maria it was neither too much love
Nor too much hate, but simply too many differences,
Different kinds of vegetables in the same pot of soup,
Unable to mix since the broth was too thick with suspicion and fear."

Having reduced the stories to their essence,
Hafez stares at the hungry pigeons staring up at him.
"I hate to say, it, Mitra Jaan, but I cannot find a common thread.
They are love stories but not the same stories."

Mitra smiles at him, sadly, and taking his hands,
Says what she is afraid to say: "Hafez Jaan, you are right,
They are three different stories,
But they are all played on the same stage.
That is what they have in common!
Tell me, my perfect lover, why didn't Majnun take Layla away,
And live free and love free, moons away from her father's tent?
Why didn't Romeo and Juliet just run away?
Just for Romeo to remain a Montague?
Just for Juliet to remain a Capulet—just for that?
Why didn't they just change their name to Macaroni
And live and love among the sheep in the mountains?
And Tony and Maria—what was that all about?
Didn't they know there were tunnels and bridges
Linking Manhattan to the rest of the world?"
Hafez, excited, finishes her analysis:
"And Adam and Eve stayed in Eden,
As if there were no fruit trees over the horizon,
Where they could live and love
Without gods or serpents telling them what to do.
And I, Hafez the Timid, suffered in Shiraz,
As if Persia were only ten feet wide and ten feet long!
Yes, my sun, my moon, my brilliant flame of Zoroaster!
Those other lovers had only to join hands and flee.
Yes, they would be without the wealth of their families,
Without the comforts of their communities.
Their love would have been their wealth!
Their love could have been their comfort!
Who says two wild bees cannot

Make wonderful honey without a comb?"

And so Hafez rushes off to Pirooz's apartment,
And gathers the money he has earned driving cab,
And Mitra rushes to her mother's apartment,
And fills a suitcase with clothes and twenty dollar bills,
The guilt money her parents paid her as penalty for their absence.
And as the sun climbs to the top of the Empire State Building,
To balance like a ball on the building's high beak,
Hafez and Mitra and the yellow taxi
Fly across the Queensboro Bridge,
And soar and soar, a pair of Firebirds on fire,
She free of her chains, he no longer trapped in his grave,
Across Long Island, ever east, ever away.

13 Flight of the Firebirds

And so ever east the Firebirds fly,
Ever east across Sunnyside, Forest Hills and Jamaica,
Ever east across Hempstead, Levittown and Massapeaqua,
Ever east across the ever-flattening hills,
The sun at their backs, the future in front of them.

Hafez watches the meter spin, joking:
"I hope we don't have to pay for this."
"We will have to pay," answers Mitra,
"But even if the meter spins until it explodes,
Our freedom will be worth the price."
They laugh, then fall silent, then Mitra whispers:
"My secure empty life is ended, I fear.
Love has filled the emptiness and danger has deposed my security.
But uncertainty is lurking everywhere for me,
Since I know little about what is coming to me,
And I know even less about *you* coming to me.
Hafez Jaan, I think I know the poet I love
More than the person I love!
I want to know more about Hafez the man,
More and more about the much that I don't know.
I don't know where I'm going,
But I want to know with whom I'm going!
Can you keep your mind on the road awhile,
While my mind reaches for your mind,
With the wiggling fingers of my curiosity?"

Hafez pats her knee, wanting to pat higher,
But knowing now is not the time.

"Yes, yes, Mitra Jaan, I can drive with or without my mind.
I've been doing it since you stole my mind,
Since the wind blew up your skirt,
And created a tornado inside my mind,
And your brains clobbered me like a hurricane,
And your grace and your art tore over me like a tidal wave.
Yes, I can drive without my mind—if you do not mind.
So storm away, Mitra Jaan, storm away!"

Mitra curls up on the seat and wraps her arms around his arm,
"I am so happy today, Hafez, and I know you are happy,
Yet you seem more somber than me, why?"
Answers Hafez: "If Pirooz is right about what the national religion
Can do to me for running off with you,
Then indeed I should be somber—
As somber as the time my home was sacked for my blasphemy,
For that ancient day and this new day seem so much alike.
Yes, I am happy at the moment—as happy as I could ever be.
Now please, my Mitra Jaan, you speak your mind, too!"

Mitra does: "In your first life, did you ever have a lover like me?"
Hafez sighs: "Had I a lover like you, Mitra Jaan,
Would I have been longing for your midnight arrival in my poem?
You are my only true love, in two lives and one death,
And one endless desert of dryness, cactuses and fixed stars.
You are my dream of dreams coming true."
"But you were married—surely you loved your wife."
"It was a marriage arranged," Hafez says.
"And before I was married to my wife, I knew not my wife.
And when I lived with my wife, I wished I never had a wife!"
Mitra smiles and asks: "That is why you longed for me?"
"Yes, Mitra Jaan, that is why I longed for you,
And longed long for you and me together."
"Hafez Jaan, you have been alive and dead for a long time.

What do you know of love?"

He shrugs: "No one knows love, its origin, its how and why.

If God is the origin of love, then He must be the origin of hate, too.

I love the Creator and His creations—especially his creation of you!

Your love frees me from longing, makes me feel belonging,

To the heart of God and the heart of Man.

Your love for me empowers me to create like a god,

And to be a god, and change the world like a god."

Hafez takes a deep breath and adds:

"Just hearing myself say these things tells me I'm no longer the old Hafez.

Our love, it seems, is the mother of a new me!"

Mitra is not satisfied by his answer: "All this god-talk, Hafez!

I want to hear your thoughts on lust,

On the kind of love you showed me last night."

Hafez grins like a gazelle in rut.

"I confess that I've lusted for the pleasure of the skin, too.

But skinly pleasure only, is self-love only.

Still, when one hears a lover's name,

Or when the mind imagines or the eyes see

A lover's naked body in the moon's naked light,

The heart loses all interest in God's steady beat,

And palpitates like a fig tree full of monkeys,

Proving—if proof is needed—the unity of the body and spirit."

Mitra touches Hafez where the driver of a car,

Flying on a fast freeway, should not be touched.

"How much do you lust for me, Hafez Jaan?"

"More than all the lusters combined, Mitra Jaan."

Mitra squeezes her hand:

"Then prove it, old poet! Prove it now!

Stop for the night, before it is night.

Aim your taxi for the next motel."

Hafez is astonished by her demand: "Mitra! What have I unlocked?
I see now why Stravinsky's monster kept his women in chains!"
"Then we are not going to stop, Hafez Jaan?"
"Did I say that? Of course we are going to stop!
At the very next motel, as soon as you explain what a *motel* is!"
She explains, and then says: "You are such a puzzle to me,
A beautiful young man hiding a dirty old man,
A man filled with so many questions and so much doubt,
Who, nevertheless, is unquestionably devout.
Tell me about your faith, Hafez Jaan."
He answers: "This poem of mine says it all:

Do as you wish but do no harm.
For, in my faith there is no other sin."

"But the books say you are a Muslim, Hafez."

"Yes, yes, I am a Muslim, but in name only,
For I sin left, right and center,
According to the list of sins the mullahs keep under their turbans.
I drank wine and will drink wine.
Just the other morning at breakfast I gobbled
An entire package of sausages, making a horrible pig of myself.
And now I make love to you, Mitra Jaan,
Before I am married to you.
I deny both free will and sin.
Except the hurting sin, which is the only sin.
I curse the clergy, the lowest and the highest.
I pretend to believe in a faith
Which is impossible to keep faith with.
I rarely go to the mosque or Friday prayer.
I don't understand what is meant by *repentance*,
I do not repent who I am!
I want to turn Creation upside down,

160

Change the order of things, even the human soul.
For all my earthbound blasphemies, Mitra Jaan,
When I died, God welcomed me without reprimanding me.
He granted Rumi and me our wish to count the stars.
Ah, Mitra-Mitra Jaan, I could confess to you mile after mile,
Until the last pebble of Long Island, about my sins according to Islam."
Says Mitra: "But you know the Koran by heart."
Hafez corrects her: "That speaks for my memory only.
I know a lot of things by heart fully—
Look, Mitra! There is one of your motels!
And look Mitra, my taxi is driving us there, all by itself,
As if my hands were not on the wheel and my foot not on the gas."

They laugh as Hafez pretends the cab, against his will,
Sweeps them off the highway and into the parking lot.
"Today our Mecca is this motel it seems," he says.
"Tomorrow our Mecca will be where
Love is God, and truth is a prophet,
And beauty and justice are the wings of all believers."

The night is another night to remember,
So intoxicating and powerful that their love
Smiles the smile of the great Persian king Cyrus,
Conqueror of Lydia and Babylon,
Friend to many many faiths and nations.

The previous night the lovers had lost their inhibitions.
So tonight is the night to demystify and gratify their curiosity,
To journey into the sparkling infinity, to turn dreams into reality.
It is a night to verify all possibilities bestowed by evolution,
All possibilities bestowed by imagination.
It is a night for exploration and satisfaction,
For two thirsty bodies to drink from each other,
Until reaching the highest peak of joyful exhaustion,

Until their spent flesh came to rest on airborne lilies,
Until their spent souls drowned in a sacred intoxication,
Until their breath was the purest desire,
Until their heartbeats beat in unison with the heartbeat of nature.

It is a night for two brilliant minds,
And two brilliant bodies, resurrected and insurrected,
To tangle unimaginably intense expressions and affections,
In the most tender and creative ways.
It is a night when the angels of love, driven mad with curiosity,
Burst through the closed door to give their permission,
And offer their suggestions,
And to smile with great satisfaction, that
Hafez and Mitra have journeyed beyond their expectations at last.
It is a night for ascendancy, for the triumph of universal love,
To make this spinning earth, if for only a moment,
This insignificant corner of existence,
The very spot where the Big Bang banged,
Where life was born and is reborn unceasingly.

In the morning they find a diner and eat waffles,
Topped with blueberries and fresh cream.
Whispers Mitra across the table: "Hafez Jaan, I think last night
We made up for all the unrequited
And unconsummated loves in history."
"And made a bit of history ourselves," adds Hafez.

And so they drive on,
Ever east across Babylon and Islip and North Patchague,
Ever east across Shinnecock Bay and Bridgehampton,
Ever east across the flat sand and high grass,
To Montauk Point and the endless Atlantic.
Along the way they buy fresh bread and fruit,

Cold Pepsi-Colas and soft French cheese.
They find a spot on the beach to eat and sleep and remember.
The sand is soft and yielding, the nodding grasses stand guard,
The blue sky hugs them with warmth and zephyr.

In the afternoon they see a man in a baggy windblown jacket,
With a paintbox and canvasses,
Winding through the starfish and driftwood towards them.
With the most trusting eyes and sweetest smile, he inquires:
"May I interrupt your great joy with the joy of remembrance?"
Says Mitra: "We have precious little money to pay for a painting."
Answers the painter: "And I have precious little need for money,
But I see you do have enough food for an army.
Let me fill my belly and I will fill one of my canvases
With a portrait of your love, which I promise you will love."

Mitra and Hafez agree to the terms,
And the painter sits on the sand and readies his palette.
He introduces himself as Bob Oyster,
And helps himself to an apple, saying between big bites:
"Seeing you together against the sky and the sea,
Is the loveliest sight in sight—are the two of you married?"
"No," says Hafez, "But that is our plan."
Asks the painter: "An immediate plan or a long-range plan?"
Hafez does not like the question:
Is this stranger with trusting eyes and the sweetest smile
Suggesting that their love is temporary and insincere?
"Immediately as soon as we can manage," he says sharply.
"That is wonderful!" says the painter.
"I just happen to be a man who marries people—
When not looking for seashells or people to paint, that is."
"You are a minister?" asks Mitra eagerly.
"Goodness no! Only a village clerk," the painter says.
"I also sell dog licenses and collect parking fines."

163

Hafez and Mitra study each other's eyes, until their hearts talk.
"Can you marry us now, Bob Oyster?" asks Hafez.

"Certainly, as soon as the portrait is finished," says the painter.
"No," says Mitra, "Marry us first.
I want us to be husband and wife in paint as well as in life."

The painter's trusting eyes and sweet smile turn to Hafez.
"That is what you wish, too?"
Says Hafez: "How could I possibly have another wish?"
The painter reaches into his jacket and pulls out a bundle of forms.
They sign where he says to sign, and on the bottom line
He scribbles BOB OYSTER as if he were the John Hancock of God.
"Now for the ceremony," he says. Do you . . ."

"Wait," says Hafez.
"Marry us while we are in the sea naked and clean,
Free of all national religions, boundaries and laws."
The painter is flummoxed: "Naked? In the water?"
They beg him and he reluctantly agrees.

Hafez and Mitra join hands and wade into the water,
And in just a few steps are up to their shoulders.
They remove their clothes and toss them to the shore.
"Make the ceremony as beautiful as our love," Hafez demands.
Promises the painter:
"I will try to make it as beautiful as the two of you."
First he asks them to dunk, to come up as fresh children,
A cleansing, a baptism, a new beginning,
For two who have become one.
Then he says: "By the authority of the creator of all things—
Of the seas and skies, all lives and all lights,
By the authority of the creator of love,

And by the authority of love itself,
I announce that the two of you have married the two of you,
And now are not two but just one of you."

Hafez and Mitra hold their faces close,
And gasp softly—as the very first creatures
To crawl ashore surely must have gasped.
The painter continues:
"Now kiss one another, for all the universe to see,
The proof of your love, your love of all loves."
Hafez and Mitra embrace and kiss.
And kiss and kiss, and kiss and kiss.
Their kiss sparkles across the applauding waves,
Inviting the fish to dance and the seagulls to sing.
"Even for Long Island that is a long kiss," laughs the painter.

The painter tosses them their clothes,
And turns around so they can dress and wade ashore,
Soaking wet but supremely happy.
Then he joins them on the beach,
And while the ocean foam teases his shoeless feet,
He kisses their foreheads, wishing them a never-ending vasal.
Hafez raises his brows: "Bob Oyster? You know this word vasal?
This ancient word of unity and fruition?"
The painter is surprised: "I thought everybody knew this word!"
He retreats to his canvas, quickly getting busy with his brushes.
"Let me capture you in a kiss," he calls out.
And so they kiss the longest of all Long Island kisses yet,
As the painter paints and paints.

When the painting is finished, and most of the food gone,
The painter summons them with his impatient arm.
"What do you think?" he asks.
Mitra looks at the painting and cries.

Hafez looks at the painting and smiles.
The painter has not only captured their faces, but also their souls:
Mitra's young and perfect soul, his old and rebellious soul.

Hafez bends and puts his lips to the painter's ear,
And whispers in the faintest of whispers:
"Thank you, Mowlana, old friend."

The afternoon eases into evening, evening into night.
The ocean resurrects the moon,
And sends it ever higher into the ever darkening sky.
To watch it, Hafez and Mitra must ever lift their chins higher.

"We must find a motel soon," Hafez says.
Mitra, resting in his arms, on a sandy knoll,
Teases him with an elbow-poke in the ribs.
"A motel? We've been married not even one night
And romance is leaving you the first night?
I want to stay here tonight, to pretend just for one night,
That this is the only night that ever existed,
That you and I are the only lovers who ever existed,
And this beach is the only love bed that ever existed."
"But the shore gets cold at night, Mitra Jaan," worries Hafez.
"We will freeze into the only ice cream cones that ever existed."
"Then we can camp out in the cab," she says.
"That back seat is big enough to hold our love, don't you think?
If we get cold, we can hold each other closer, like clawless cats."
"But Mitra, my wife! It isn't safe! Hungry crabs the size of whales
Might crawl from the sea and devour us in our yellow can.
Clams the size of alligators might drill
Right though the seat and pinch us to death!"
Mitra laughs: "You are being silly, Hafez Jaan."
"Silly but not so silly, my wife," he laughs back.

"Spending the night here could be dangerous,
And more than likely against the national religion."

Mitra is all the more persistent:
"You run away with me and marry me,
And suddenly you are worried about danger and me?
Suddenly you are worried about laws?
Hafez Jaan, I want to cuddle up with you in
The backseat of your taxi tonight—and nothing will stop me,
Not the big bad dogma, not alligators or gods.
And don't worry about the crabs and clams, my husband,
Nothing could penetrate the skin of that cab."

Hafez's reservation remains and he resists even as he resigns:
"First you demand this, and then you demand that!"
Mitra pulls him to his feet and spanks the sand from his bottom.
"I am a conqueror, Hafez Jaan! I admit it!
I've got the weapons and you've got the goodies.
You are my territory now—all of you is mine!"
She thunderlaughs loud enough to wake the plastic owls
Dangled from trees to scare woodpeckers away.

Hafez allows himself to be led to the taxi.
"True, I am now more yours than I am mine.
But remember, my Western conqueror,
The East is not dead and the West not what it pretends to be."
Mitra opens the door, growling playfully:
"Enough of your Persian jibber-jab—so it is settled?"
Hafez bends his head and crawls inside. "So it is settled, Mitra."

The lovers do what lovers do, a night of paradise in the backseat,
The cab's moon-lit yellow skin cuddling
With the green scrub pines and the amber grasses,
The ocean rhythmically shooshing and shooshing,

The taxi never resting, bouncing and bouncing.

Even though she is pleased as a bee
Sucking the blossoms of a cherry,
Mitra's relentless desires flare once more for more thrills.
Just past midnight she shakes her husband.
"Are you awake my grieved old lover?"
"I am awake," he yawns, "but I don't want to be awake."
He grins a moon's grin and touches her lips with his lips,
And adds: "My ancient dream is coming true
More often than I ever could have dreamed!
Tell me what is it you wish now?"
She tells him that the sea is lonely, and that she is also lonely.
"Smell the salty mist, my love, the teardrops of the sea.
The sea is thirsting for us, the sea is weeping for us,
For us to join the sea and together with the sea become one us."

Hafez yawns again and protests:
"We are not baby turtles rushing to the sea at midnight."
But Mitra smiles and persists:
"Then why are we trapped inside this yellow shell?
I want to go skinny dipping, Hafez Jaan—please!"
These strange words puzzle Hafez.
"What is *skinny dipping*? The name of an island? A boat?
A species of fish you want to catch with your hands?"
Mitra giggles: "I want to go swimming, Hafez Jaan.
As naked as we were before!"
"In the middle of the night?" frets Hafez.
"Just because we were born and married naked, must we die naked, too?
Are you not afraid of anything?"

Mitra opens the cab door and slides out,
And pulls at him as if he was a stubborn suitcase.
"I fear nothing, not any more.

My love for you thwarts all fears,
Including the fear of ghosts, laws, or bottomless seas.
But Hafez, why are you suddenly afraid of everything?"
"Because suddenly I am Adam," he says.
"And you are suddenly a woman who talks to snakes.
You tempt me and tempt me, and tempt me,
To eat apples and pomegranates, and persimmons, too.
Wife, trust me, I am an Adam better suited to writing poems
Than picking one dangerous fruit after the other!"
Mitra laughs wickedly, seductively.
"You *are* my Adam, Hafez, and I am your Eve,
And in this Eden of ours, I am God and Satan combined!
You will taste my fruit or any fruit I command!"
Hafez is serious now:
"I want to be commanded, tempted into submission.
But I also want us to be cautious, I want this to last.
Having been treated so well by fate, I fear we are tempting our fate.
Oh Mitra, my precious love, my perfect fate!
I am suddenly as a warrior returning home from the last battle,
Having fended off a thousand swords and arrows,
Suddenly afraid of slipping on a loose stone.
Come on, my wife, let's go dip our skins!"

They undress and don the moonlight—it fits them perfectly.
They run to the beach and splash into the waves,
Which embrace them voluptuously and shower them with kisses,
Soft and wet kisses, such incredibly horny kisses.
They not only see and feel the moonlight, but hear the moonlight.
The faraway lights of a ship wink at them,
And the stars sprinkle them with the sweet scent of eternity.

Hafez feels, and Mitra feels, that for the first time in history,
A love, their love, has become conscious of itself,
Conscious of its own beauty and dignity,

Conscious of its own truth, historicity, and immortality,
Ascending to the limits of all consciousness.

Their love mingles with the ocean's warm vapors of love,
Ascending higher and higher, building a staircase to their vasal,
Touching all luminous creatures in the sky,
Dancing a universal dance of love,
Singing a universal song of love,
Seducing every fire in the firmament,
To dance and sing with their love,
To make love to their love,
And give birth to numerous new stars in love.
Suddenly a shower of meteors
Serenades their togetherness in love.
Just as suddenly the flashing lights
Of police cars surround their love.
Hafez takes Mitra in his arms, and whispers sadly:
"I think we have just been evicted from Eden."

And how right Hafez is:
In a few minutes questions are asked and explanations rejected.
Mitra is driven home to Manhattan in one black car,
And Hafez driven to jail in the screened backseat of another.

14 Judgment Of Flanders Bay

Pirooz takes Rumi another glass of orange juice,
And another box of Kleenex,
Protecting his own nose with an empty espresso cup,
So the poet's hungry germs, propelled like microscopic rockets,
By endless screaming sneezes,
Don't crash land in his own tender insides.

The Mowlana sneezes: *"Hbleeeeech! Hbpppphhhhht!"*
Then asks: "Are you sure I shouldn't go with you today?"
"If I'm sure of anything" answers Pirooz,
"It's that you should stay put—and should've stayed put."
"Hbleeeeech! Hbpppphhhhht!
You are still blaming me for marrying Hafez?"
"No, Mowlana," Pirooz says. "I am still blaming me
For telling my problems to a pair of cactuses.
Hafez came to New York to look after me,
And you came to New York to look after him,
And here I am looking after both of you—pray-tell, Mowlana!
How ever did you think that marrying Hafez and Mitra
Would uncomplicate the complicated,
Instead of making it more complicated?"

"Hbleeeeech! Hbpppphhhhht!
I know you are forever worried about the law, Pirooz,
And wish that I had taken your side in this Mitra matter.
But as someone who has lived and died and lived again,
I am more worried about God's law than man's law.
Hafez and Mitra love each other truly,
And giving themselves to each other is not

The bad thing you think it is—*Hbleeeeech! Hbpppphhhhht!*

"So take poor Hafez to Long Island," Rumi says
As Pirooz circles the bed, filling the sick air with a spray of Lysol.
"And let the judge judge him as he will.
Rape is a heinous crime,
But the love of Hafez and Mitra is not a crime."

And so Pirooz piles Hafez into the taxi,
And drives east across the Queensboro Bridge.
Hafez brings with him a pile of Pirooz's books,
To read on the way, and if the judge decrees,
To read in jail for the rest of his second life.
Pirooz glances at the book Hafez is reading.
It is a book on America and what went wrong.
He says: "Do not expect things not to go wrong."
Hafez replies without looking up: "It will go as well as it can."
Says Pirooz: "More than likely as bad as it can."
Hafez shrugs. "Then it will go as bad as it can.
Either way makes no difference.
I will still love Mitra and she will still love me!"
"Given the trouble you are in, Hafez," Pirooz scowls,
"You are handling this all very well."
Hafez answers with a little shrug:
"I have some experience with trouble
From my former life."
Now the poet looks up from his book,
And watches the cars flying west as they fly east.
"Pirooz Jaan, inside I am crying the tears of a thousand orphans.
I am frightened, already locked in jail,
Already trapped inside the saddest poem ever written.
Already missing Mitra as Majnun missed Layla.
How many lives and deaths before man is kinder to mankind?"

172

Three months have passed since the early morning
When Hafez called from a jail cell in Flanders Bay.
Three days he sat in that cell as the charges piled up against him:
Statutory rape, theft of a taxi, going naked on a public beach.
And two months have passed since Mitra's mother
Came to Pirooz's apartment,
And thinking Pirooz was Hafez, kicked him on the shin,
And informed him that her daughter would be a mother soon.
Pirooz explained who he was, and took the woman in his arms,
For she was suddenly crying and shaking,
And saying in the voice of a wounded sparrow,
"My baby is a woman and I am no mother at all."

His kicked shin still throbbing, Pirooz took her into the kitchen,
And made her tea, and held her hand, and listened to her life
As it tumbled from her quivering lips.
She was a beautiful woman, Mitra plus a few short years,
And Pirooz struggled hard to keep his mind
Where, under the circumstances, it should be.

With news that her daughter was carrying a baby,
Mitra's mother pleaded that the charges be dropped.
But the prosecutor persisted, saying that the law was the law,
And baby or no baby, a girl is a girl,
That the good people of Suffolk County
Cannot permit the likes of this foreigner
To prey on America's impressionable young.

All rise for the judge, who floats wearily to his bench,
And looks out, over the top of his glasses,
As if he were a barn owl watching mice from the rafters.
He studies the defendant, the young Mr. Hafez,

And wonders how such an innocent-looking lad
Could have perpetrated such a heinous offense.
After shuffling his papers and blowing his nose,
He asks the prosecutor to begin.

The prosecutor fills his cheeks with air, as if his head were a balloon,
And states the state's case: "Your honor,
According to the statutes a rape has occurred,
And given that Mr. Hafez has already admitted
Doing what the law says he has done,
And given that medical tests show
He did indeed do what he says he has done,
The prosecution's work is also done—we rest our case."
His balloon head empty of air, he proudly sits down,
Satisfied that he has demonstrated aptly
That this Mr. Hafez is a bad man in a good world,
Satisfied that in the next election he can convince voters
That *he* is a good man in a not-good world.

The judge swings his owl eyes toward the defendant.
"Mr. Hafez, it is your turn.
Do you still intend to represent yourself?"
Hafez stands and clears his throat: "Your honor,
I will not only represent myself, but *be* myself.
After all, who knows better than me
That I am innocent of everything but love?"
Says the judge: "I remind you once more, Mr. Hafez,
These charges could put you in prison for a very long time.
Just because the cab company has forgiven you for taking their cab,
And just because the park rangers have punished you
With only a warning for bathing naked on a public beach,
The County of Flanders Bay will not be so gentle.
Should you be found guilty you will be genuinely punished."
"I genuinely understand," answers Hafez.

"Then proceed, Mr. Hafez."

And so, as Pirooz sits with his head in his hands,
As Mitra rubs her slowly swelling belly,
As Mitra's mother twists a tear-soaked handkerchief,
Hafez begins his defense: "I will call three witnesses today:
One to testify on the cause of my trouble,
One to testify on my innocence,
And one to attest to my good character."

The balloon-headed prosecutor objects:
"What has caused him to commit this crime
Has no bearing on the fact that he has committed it."
"Overruled," rules the judge. "Mr. Hafez, proceed."
Says Hafez: "I call Mr. Omar Khayyam."

Eyes look everywhere, But no witness is found.
"Where is this Mr. Khayyam?" asks the judge.
Hafez, as if taking a nap in another world,
Blinks and then bows as if the judge were a king.
"Forgive me, your honor, here is my witness."
He takes a small book out of his coat.
"This is Mr. Khayyam, or what is left of Mr. Khayyam."
He hands the book to the seemingly bewildered judge.
Says the judge: "This is the *Rubbaiyyt*
Of the old Persian poet—just what is your point, Mr. Hafez?"
"Well, your honor, since Mr. Khayyam has been dead awhile,
I will recite his testimony myself.
I have marked the pages so you can read along."
The prosecutor's head again balloons: "Objection!"
"Overruled," rules the judge. "Mr. Hafez, proceed."
And so Hafez recites:

"If I had been asked, I would have refused my birth.

If asked, I would refuse my death.
I would forswear all that there is: the coming, the being, the going."

Hafez waits for the judge to find the next page,
Then says: "Mr. Khayyam also testifies that,

"God knew full well all my future acts
When he brought me forth into these facts.
I am able to do nothing beyond His will."

Booms the balloon-headed prosecutor: "Your honor,
'God told me to do it' is not a recognizable defense!"
Says the judge: "What evidence to judge,
And whether to judge it, is for me to judge."
He pushes his head across the wide bench,
And to everyone's surprise, recites a verse of Khayyam himself:

"Drink now while you live,
For once buried under the earth you shall sleep forever,
Without foe, without friend, without folks, without lovers."

Then the judge says with a wry smile: "You see, Mr. Hafez,
Mr. Khayyam had doubts himself about
The determinism you raise in your defense.
Otherwise he wouldn't suggest to you and me,
That we do this or that as we please."
Says the startled Hafez: "Now I object!
I am the one presenting the evidence!"
The judge ignores him, saying,
"But even if I accept that all is pre-determined—
That man's actions are merely God gibber-jabbering to Himself,
To absolve Himself from Himself,
For inducing you to do what you have done—
Are not the laws that man creates the laws God wants?

And if the answer is *yes*, Mr. Hafez,
Has it not then been pre-determined
That I must not only judge you guilty,
But also God guilty, as a co-conspirator in the rape of this girl?"

Booms the balloon-headed prosecutor: "Your honor, please!
This is highly irregular, and confusing, too!
Do you wish me to charge God in this affair as well?"
Answers the judge: "If God wants us to charge Him,
He will let us know.
Meanwhile the prosecution may, if it wishes,
Cross-examine Mr. Khayyam's little book."

The prosecutor rises, his head not swelling at all.
"No questions, your honor."
"Then," says the judge, "Mr. Hafez will call his next witness."
Says Hafez with a smile: "I call Professor Pirooz."

Pirooz, surprised, springs to his feet,
And on shaky legs struggles to the stand,
Where he hears himself swear to tell the truth,
The whole truth, and nothing but the truth,
Knowing that if he does tell the truth,
No one would believe the truth!
How can he say that this young Hafez is really the old Hafez?
How can he say this Hafez has been twice a man and once a cactus?
So he tells the judge that he has known Hafez since a child,
Which is someway true, someway false,
Since he doesn't say who was the *child*, Hafez or him!

Before Hafez can ask him a question,
Pirooz shushes him with a finger to his lips,
And addresses the judge: "Your honor,
I agree with the prosecutor that this trial so far

Is both irregular and confusing.
And since it is, may I say something about this determinism,
About which you and Mr. Hafez disagree?"
"Objection!" both the prosecutor and Hafez shout.
"Overruled," rules the judge. "Mr. Pirooz, proceed."

Pirooz thanks the judge and begins: "Your honor,
Physics, evolution, and history make some actions impossible,
Like holding this court in the Andorra galaxy.
This is *absolute determinism*—a pre-determined impossibility.
Local religions, cultures, and laws produce *relative determinism*—
The degree of difficulties a person must overcome
To do what he wishes to do, or not to do what he wishes not to do.
Just as there are two types of determinism,
There are two types of laws—absolute laws and relative laws.
Laws are constantly re-formed, sometimes even reversed.
So what Mr. Hafez is saying, I think,
Is not that he is innocent, but that he is innocently guilty
Of a law which should not exist."
Pirooz now turns to Hafez: "Is this not what you are saying?"

Answers Hafez with a frown:
"Mr. Pirooz, I called you to defend me, not make excuses for me.
Mitra and I did what we were both designed to do
And what we both wished to do.
All this legal talk is just seeds rattling in an empty gourd."
The judge interrupts him:
"Human design is not the only thing that matters here, Mr. Hafez.
There is the matter of the laws."
Hafez turns to the bench and opens his arms,
As if welcoming an arrow.
"Your honor, I am guilty of only one thing—of love!"
The balloon-head of the prosecutor swells.
"Again the defendant defends rape as love,

And insults the court to boot!"
Says the judge: "The court is not insulted. Professor Pirooz, go on."

Pirooz feels himself wilting,
As if his bottom were the roots of a melon plant,
And his chair a pile of dry rocks.
"As you can see your honor,
Mr. Hafez comes from a world very different from here!
I, too, was born in Iran,
When my mother was only fourteen years old.
All was heavenly, legal, and good.
I assure you I am legitimate!
And Mr. Hafez, too, is legitimate—
A legitimately good person, legitimately in love with Mitra.
Regardless of his age or hers,
They did make a vow of marriage good for any age."
The prosecutor's head nearly bursts:
"Vows to an impostor you mean!"
Answers Pirooz: "They believed what Bob Oyster was telling them,
Just as you believe what the law is telling you."

Hafez is growing impatient with Pirooz.
"Professor, please! Tell the judge about the national religion!"
Pirooz suddenly wishes he had some of the prosecutor's air.
"It is just a silly theory, your honor."
Says the judge: "Silly or not, the counsel for the defense
Wants the court to hear it—which indeed it does!
Enlighten us, professor."
So Pirooz proceeds to describe the national religion,
The Constitution as the new Holy Book, and all the rest,
Finishing thus: "It is self-evident that concerning age and sex
The precepts of the national religion violate
Both the will of Nature and God,
Making this court more illegal than Hafez's behavior."

Hafez is delighted: "Absolutely correct!
It is I who should be finding the law guilty,
Not the law finding me guilty.
Now, professor, tell the judge about the First Prime Rule!"
Pirooz winces, as he talks picturing himself
Rotting in the jail cell next to Hafez.
"The First Prime Rule is that all man-made rules die,
And are replaced by new rules,
Imposed by man-made human gods
Who have replaced the God-made God.
And the Second Prime Rule is that the First Prime Rule
Is an exception to itself and immortal.
So, Hafez is being prosecuted under a law which
Later will be prosecuted itself!"

The judge scratches his chin: "Are not both laws disobeyed at peril?"
The question makes Pirooz feel like the professor he is.
"Your honor, attraction and love have many dimensions,
Some good some bad:
Physical—like the attraction of magnet and iron.
Chemical—like that of hydrogen and oxygen.
Biological—like that of sperms and eggs.
Social—like attraction to status, intellect, power, and wealth.
Spiritual—like that of one kindred spirit to another.
Ecstatic—like infatuation with beauty and human possibilities.
Local rules and laws and even religions,
Always temporary like seasons and flies,
Are unable to control these permanent
And prominent and imponderable pre-dispositions of man.
Someday this very prosecution will be thought a witchhunt
By the new high priests of a new national religion,
Like so many previous witchhunts in history.
In short, your honor, love must be understood, not chained

Just to please those who have never experienced its ecstasy."

"Have you questions for the professor?"
The judge asks the prosecutor.
The prosecutor lifts himself just half way.
"Just at what college he teaches, so I never send my son there!"
Everyone laughs, Pirooz the hardest.
Then the courtroom falls as silent and cold and sad
As an empty refrigerator.
Whispers the judge: "Mr. Hafez, proceed."
Says Hafez: "I call my final witness, Miss Susan M. Smith."

From the back of the room walks a very old lady,
Badly bending over a bamboo cane, wearing the floppiest of hats,
Its brim alive with a band of yellow roses.
Her white curly hair covers her wrinkly white skin.
Her baggy print dress descends from her chin to her heels.
Still, her blue eyes are dancing with exuberance and vitality.
Only on the outside is this old lady old.
The bailiff, the judge, all in the courtroom,
Treat her with the greatest patience and respect,
For at her age she has earned such esteem.

Begins Hafez: "Miss Smith please tell the court
What you know of the man wrongly charged."
She says this: "I have known the defendant
Since he arrived in New York,
And not knowing our currency,
Trusted me to make my own change
When he drove me here or there.
Look into his eyes, your honor:
Are they not the eyes of a trusting man?
Are they not the eyes of an honest man?
Are they not the eyes of a caring man?

Do they not gleam with creativity and intelligence?
Do they not thirst for knowledge,
Truth, and the truest kinds of love?
Can anyone honestly say that those eyes
Should be looking out through iron bars?
Can anyone honestly say that Mitra was wrong
To fall in love with those eyes or the sweet soul peering out?"

Hafez knows that his face is as red as a radish.
"Thank you, Miss Smith, I have no further questions."
The judge swings his own owl eyes to the prosecutor.
"She is your witness," he says.
The prosecutor rises and approaches,
His head swelling with questions as he walks.
He nods respectfully at the witness,
And speaks in the soft tone he reserves for his grandmother.
"Miss Smith, can you please tell us what the accused does
For a living, this creative and intelligent, thirsty man?"
"Well, he drives a taxi."
"A taxi you say?"
"And writes some pretty good poems," the old lady angrily adds.
The prosecutor chuckles softly: "So does my ten-year-old son."
Says the old lady: "I hope you aren't going to jail him, too."
Everyone laughs and the judge bangs his gavel.
The prosecutor's head seems to lose air, as if punctured by a wasp.
"Miss Smith, with all respect due,
Your Mr. Hafez can't make change,
Can't count past the age of fifteen,
Can't keep on his clothes or learn the laws all others know.
And yet you say he's as smart as they come?
Can you give the court one single example
Of this taxi driver's great mental gifts?"

The old lady glares through her curls.

Then her eyes soften and her lips rise into a confident smile.
"Well, for one thing, Mr. Hafez knows both
The Holy Bible and the Holy Koran by heart, every word of them,
And is able to provide the most profound interpretations of each."
Says the balloon-headed prosecutor: "Every word, Miss Smith?
While I'm sure you believe it's true—"
Answers the old lady: "I believe it's true because it is true."
Now the judge intervenes:
"It is easy to test her belief—we do have a Bible here."
Hafez is surprised: "And not a Koran?"
"Unfortunately, no," answers the judge.
"But I will ask you a question that
Someone familiar with both should know."
The judge takes the bailiff's Bible, and folds himself over it,
So no one can see what pages he turns.
"Mr. Hafez" he says, "please recite for the court Genesis 17:5."
The defendant, without thinking, says:

"Neither shall thy name anymore be called Abram,
But thy name shall be Abraham;
For a father of many nations I have made thee."

The court is duly impressed, But Hafez does not stop there.
He continues to recite—
Despite the judge's banging bang-bang gavel—
Right through 17:17:

"Then Abraham fell upon his face,
And laughed, and said in his heart,
Shall a child be born unto him that is
A hundred years old? and shall Sarah,
That is ninety years old, bear?"

Hafez stops, grins at Miss Smith, and says to the prosecutor,

"You see? God cares nothing for age! Only the results of love!"
The judge pounds his gavel one last time, asking,
"Does the prosecution have more questions for the witness?"
"No, your honor."
Says the judge: "The witness may step down."

But the witness does not step down,
Instead telling the judge:
"Given the gravity of the charges against Mr. Hafez,
I wish to provide further evidence."
No matter how wide he opens his mouth,
Or squirms in his chair,
The prosecutor cannot make himself object.
So the judge smiles and says to Miss Smith:
"Who are we to deny the wisdom of a long life?"

Miss Smith springs suddenly up,
Tosses her hat and her wig of white curls.
With a swipe of her sleeve the white skin and wrinkles
Disappear from her face, the baggy dress falls away,
And like a butterfly emerging from the dingiest of cocoons,
Stands there the most beautiful of creatures,
In a silk blouse of Persian blue and a white wool skirt.
A string of small white pearls adorn her neck.
It is Mitra.

The court is rocking like a ship caught in a storm.
The judge's gavel is suddenly made of sponge,
Unable to bang anyone to civility and order.
The prosecutor, balloon-head bobbing like a leaky blimp,
Screams his objections: "Perjury! Contempt! Subterfuge! Fraud!"
While Hafez dances a proud Sama,
Pirooz and his handkerchief are busily catching
The torrent of tears dripping from Mitra's mother's eyes.

Finally the courtroom returns to quiet,
And the owl-eyed judge, as angry as the American eagle,
Demands that Mitra explain her deceit.
She says: "The prosecutor claims that I am a victim,
While all the while I know I'm the luckiest woman on earth,
For I am loved by Hafez and I love Hafez back.
The prosecutor says that Hafez must suffer,
Because there are too few birthdays in my basket of life.
But can age be the only determinant
Of physical, intellectual, emotional, or even political maturity?
From what I've seen, many *children* are more adult than adults.
Look at all the adults addicted to drugs, alcohol, tobacco, and their jobs.
Look at all the irresponsible adults in business and government.
Why is it that when children do wrong they are tried as adults,
And sentenced to life as adults?
Why is it that adults eagerly send children to fight their wars?
Why are children taxed as adults but denied the right to vote?
Why are children taught repeatedly, on every television show,
In every movie, every ad, and in every song,
That sex is good and sex is fun, and then are told to abstain?
Why are there these *magical* ages?
Do the clocks of all bodies and minds tick at the same rate?
At sixteen you can do this, at eighteen that?
Why is it that we trust our arbitrary clocks
More than the maturity measured by our biological clocks?
The Hafez before you is only a few ticks older than midnight,
And I am only a few ticks shy.
Yet Hafez must go to prison,
While his child is ticking toward birth in my womb?
Why isn't there a national test for adulthood?
An exam that encourages children to work for it?
Why aren't there different licenses
For the different attributes of adulthood?

Don't most teen-agers tinker with sex?
Should we send them all to jail?

"This court shouldn't be deciding whether Hafez is guilty.
This court should be deciding whether I'm an adult!
Shall I be permitted to pursue my happiness,
Or forced to submit to the medieval ethos of purity,
Without being permitted to enjoy the matrimonial status
That the young medievals enjoyed?
Why is my husband taken from me?
Where is our freedom in this land of the free?
When I was dressed in the dress of an old woman
Your eyes respected me, and your ears listened to me,
And your judgment accepted my judgment.
What really has changed?"

Now the judge, watching his watch,
Gives Mitra just two more minutes to conclude.
"Two minutes is plenty," says Mitra as she rises,
And starts unbuttoning her blouse.
(What now will she turn into, Pirooz wonders,
Holding Mitra's mother's hand
As if it were a hand that he himself owned.)

Says Mitra as the buttons slip open one by one:
"Hafez is not guilty of statutory rape—
I am guilty of statutory seduction!
He is the honey bee, yes, but I am the honey flower, also yes.
It was me who tempted Hafez, me who persuaded him to flee,
So judge me, judge, and set the innocent Hafez free!"

Her blouse is now open
And her mature breasts are glowing under the sun-like lights.
The prosecutor is too stunned to object.

"My breasts are not jailbait," Mitra says. "They are lovebait,
The bait Hafez took on the instruction of Nature.
Soon they will be the bait that catches a hungry child,
Which the prosecutor says I must nourish alone."
"Cover yourself!" the judge commands. "Cover yourself now!"
But Mitra does not cover herself.
Instead she reaches for the zipper that holds her skirt to her rolling hips.
There are shrieks and confusions,
Some eyes closing, some opening wide.
Again the prosecutor shouts his objections:
"Indecent! Indecent! Impudent child!"
Mitra shouts back: "It is you who have forced my private acts
To become public facts!
It is you who have forced my private parts to become public parts!"
Uniformed guards rush forward,
Awaiting the judge's instruction to haul the witness away.
Mitra's mother is wailing,
Crushing Pirooz's fingers as if they were five pods of peas.
Bang-bangy-bang goes the judge's gavel, as he screams:
"CASE DISMISSED! THE DEFENDANT IS FREE!"

All are stunned, all are silent, all are frozen in disbelief.
Squeals the prosecutor's exploding head:
"Case dismissed? What do you mean?"
The judge slides over his bench,
Grabbing Hafez and Mitra in his robe-heavy arms.
"This way! Quick!" he so orders,
"Professor Pirooz, you come with me, too!"

Pirooz asks Mitra's mother to join them
But she needs to rush to work.
So the four walk briskly from the chamber,
Down the hall toward the wide oak doors.
The guards and lawyers follow silently in awe,

But the reporters are in a frenzy.

("What a court!" one exclaims. "What truths!" exclaims another.)

"Is that your taxi?" the judge asks Hafez when they get outside.

Hafez nods and they all pile in.

Suddenly, as Hafez turns his key, the black robe of the judge

Changes into the enlightened robe of an old Persian poet.

His beard white as a baby cloud, his eyes bright like the first dawn.

Pirooz is surprised but not surprised.

"Mowlana," he asks, "whatever happened to your terrible cold?"

15 Rise Of The Techno-Sapiens

The cab takes off in a hurry,
Hafez driving, Mitra squeezing his arm,
Pirooz and Rumi bouncing in the back seat.

One eye on the road, one filling the rearview mirror,
Hafez asks, "Am I really free? Is my trial really over?"
Answers Rumi proudly: "I not only disguised myself as the judge,
But disguised all the paperwork against you as confetti."
"But even confetti can be pieced together again,"
Worries Pirooz as he watches out the back window
For police cars and helicopters, for the whole pursuing world.
Answers Rumi: "Not the confetti this spirit makes, Pirooz Jaan!"

And so they flee Flanders Bay, zig-zagging the backroads,
The cab one tiny yellow bee lost in an endless meadow of blooms.
"Should we head back to the city now?" Hafez asks his companions.
"Assuming, of course, I can find the right road?"
Pirooz answers him with this long soliloquy:
"Do we really want to rush to the city—to simmer in the melting pot,
To boil in the boiling pot, or be sewed into uneasy quilts?
I say we let the big city be.
I say we let that Big Apple glaze alone in the blue bus-fume smog,
To cough and choke and miss us,
And wonder if we are missing her in return!
I say we let the big city be.

"Let the Wall Street crapshooters, the Broadway dancers,
The Fifth Avenue jewelers and boutiquaries,
The bankers and lawyers and celebrities,

189

The Harlem jazzbos and Latino nurses,
The Canal Street vendors and Korean fruit sellers,
The accented cabbies and big-bellied Italian cops,
The street politicians and city hall preachers,
Let them all chew and chew on that apple of all unchewable apples.
I say we let the big city be.

"Let the hookers, the pimps, the drug wheeler-dealers,
The beggars, lunatics, and five-finger thieves,
The hungry artists, the tone-deaf subway virtuosos,
The skinny waiters, the stray dogs selling their fleas,
The alligators growing fat from penthouse sewerage,
Let them all be crushed in the giant garlic crusher of indifference.
I say we let the big city be.

"Let the derring-do developers nibble away at the last weedy lots.
Let the tub-thumpers and trend-setters
Devour the many mumbo-jumbo cultures,
And poop them back out into the fancy designer bedpans
That the six-figure swells can't live without.
Let the nobodies scramble for status.
Let the hidden eyes of homeless kids remain hidden even from God.
Let the blond girls shop and the ghetto gangs bang bang.
Let problems smolder and hostilities fester and blow.
Now tell me, Hafez Jaan, and the rest of you jaans,
Do you really want to rush back to the big garlic crusher,
To be crushed at this very shining moment of our relief?
Or shall we let the big city be?"

It is Mitra who answers: "You're right, Pirooz! Let's go to the beach!"

Hafez squeezes the wheel nervously.
"The beach again, Mitra Jaan?
The beach has gotten us into such trouble already."

She kisses him loud on the cheek, saying,
"This time we'll have Rumi and Pirooz to make us behave."
Wonders Hafez: "And who is going to make them behave?"
She kisses him again, even louder yet.
"Me, me—I will make them!
So quit making objections and start looking for directions!
We all need an afternoon by the sea, to touch the openness together
And together feel our togetherness.
We need the waves, the winds, and the sun's bountiful beams,
Bewitching us to think of love and a wedding."
"Not another wedding," Rumi implores.
"Oh yes!" says Mitra, "a wedding of the whales!
A bride covered in watery lace, a nervous groom in pursuit,
A splashing good procession of family and friends.
My parents used to bring me to the Long Island shore,
To picnic and pose for pictures with the whales.
I used to imagine their frolicking as a wedding in the waves."

"It is too bad we don't have a picnic," says Pirooz.
"Some sandwiches or something."
"Or a bottle of whisky," adds Hafez.
Rumi scolds him: "The last thing we need is getting drunk."
"Not whisky to get drunk," says Hafez,
"Just to sip a bit, to make us sparkle inside,
So we can understand the sparkling sea outside,
And toast the end of our troubles on every side
And fly to the up side!
Just a little whisky so we can raise our little glasses,
And sing to each other, 'Salaamati! Salaamati! Salaamati!'
(To your heath! To your health! To your health!)

Now Hafez sings, as if he already has had a few sips:
"Wine is good but whisky is the winner.
Love of God is good but love of Mitra is *gooder*.

Didn't Mitra happen in God's mind before she happened in my mind?
So my love for Mitra is also my love for God's mind.
And God on the eighth day tasted some whisky in his mind,
And said to Himself, 'This is pretty good stuff!'
So He willed the *possibility* for whisky
Before anyone on earth could make or even think of whisky.

"Yes, that is the way it is with God.
He tests all things in his mind before creating their possibility.
Me. Mitra. Love. All were once possibility, only possibility.
Garlic crushers. Whisky. Sin. Also once possibility.
God even tested the possibility of Himself before Creating Himself!"

Hafez's singing is soon joined by the singing of the seagulls.
They roll down their windows and taste the salty wind.
Then suddenly the cab coughs and quivers to a stop.
Rumi jokes: "God has just imagined a broken car
And sent us its possibility on a lightening bolt.
See where your blasphemy has gotten us, Hafez Jaan?"

"Blasphemy?" squeaks Hafez. "I was just teasing God back a bit."
Rumi laughs: "And now God is teasing us just a bit."
Pirooz rebuts: "No, No! This is not God teasing us,
This is technology—the new god—that is teasing us."

Mitra is impatient to reach the beach. "Please just fix the car, Hafez,
Before Rumi and Pirooz suck you into another endless debate!"
Hafez looks at her as if she was someone who did not know him.
"Me fix the car, Mitra Jaan? That is like asking a dead man
To dig his own grave and then cover himself up.
I am not a mechanic, Mitra Jaan!
I drive my cab, watch Pirooz's TV, talk on Pirooz's phone,
Switch on this and switch off that, switch switch and switch.
But don't ask me what makes the switches work for me.

192

When it comes to the magic of modernity I am as broken as this car."
Mitra looks to Rumi. "How about you, Mowlana?
Can you change yourself into a mechanic?"
Rumi is nervous with uncertainty.
"If you want me to look like a mechanic, I will conjure one up.
But don't expect that mechanic to mend the car.
You'll remember when I was a brown boy flying a kite that kite crashed."
So Mitra twists toward Pirooz. "Can you fix it, professor?"
She knows the second she asks that she shouldn't have asked,
For he immediately does what he does best—talks and talks.

Talks Pirooz: "Modern man is addicted to technology.
It is a fatal addiction, like that of pink lungs for oxygen.
Without gauges and gadgets, wheels, turbines, and computers,
Modernity, and all humanity, must lie down and die."
After a pause to gulp some air,
Pirooz squeaks excitedly like an adolescent boy:
"And I'm not saying anything about tapwater, gas, and electricity!
The great techno-trinity of techno-civility!"
Those words—and the way he says them—make the others laugh.
Pirooz laughs, too—then laughs more as he continues:
"An opium addict has no idea how the opium actually works.
And ordinary folks have no clue how a machine works.
Computers do go blank.
Ships sink, planes crash, cars sputter and stop when needed most."

Hafez pops the hood and all four stare at the hot naked engine
—its tubes and wires and all the magical thingamabobs—
As if their collective gaze might miraculously bring it to life.
Pirooz, wearing a mischievous smile, says:
"How I wish I could pile everything my hands cannot fix,
And all the things my mind cannot grasp,
And every question my lectures cannot explain,
Into a big garlic crusher and throw the switch—

Which, of course, given my luck, would not switch!"
Offers Rumi: "Our handicrafts are defective because we are defective."
Pirooz, jiggling all the wires he can reach, answers thus:
"Yes, your God's handicrafts are the most defective of all.
The human genome, for example,
Contains thousands of disease-causing imperfections.
Do you suppose your God made man's genes in the image of his own?"
Rumi joins him in jiggling the wires.
"My God? Please don't make me responsible for God, Pirooz.
I'm not even sure if God has genes, let alone defective ones."

Mitra, losing all hope in these squeaking, do-nothing Persians,
Shakes her head and suggests: "Maybe the car is simply out of gas."
Says Hafez: "Do you take me for a fool, my illegal wife?
The first thing I did was check the gas gauge—the tank is half full."
"Perhaps the gauge is broken," Mitra says.
"Don't be silly," says Hafez.
But Pirooz agrees with her: "Gauges are undependable
Since the people who make them are undependable.
But whether it's the gauge or these wires and tubes,
We are still a long way from home!
So, what do we do with these unwilling wheels?"

Mitra, shaking her head, pulls the cellphone from her purse,
Saying as she hands it to Pirooz, "Either pray or call a garage."
So Pirooz calls the operator, who connects him to a garage.
For twenty minutes the invisible god on the other end
Inundates him with all sorts of silly questions,
Pushing the professor nearly to madness.
Finally the god promises a towtruck in an hour or two.

Pirooz hands the phone back to Mitra,
Grumbling and making faces at the frustration he feels:
"The voice demanded all my numbers—my phone, VISA, address, age.

It stopped short, thank God, of asking for the date of my death!
Friends, we still have one soul, but it is seen as two persons:
The biological person we know and the electronic blip others know.
Our pants are electronically down! Way, way down!"
"Then I hope the electronic police aren't around," jokes Hafez.

"Well," Mitra tells them, "We wanted to go to the beach,
And here we are at the beach,
Beached like four unhappy boats for an hour or two.
So let's enjoy the afternoon."
So they head for the shore, finding a magnificent ribbon of sand.
The sight of so many near-naked people makes Hafez crack:
"Why aren't the national religion cops here, making arrests?"

They take off their shoes and walk arm-in-arm,
Enjoying the naked waves making love to their naked ankles.
Soon their blue mood disappears into the happy blue of the sky.
Hafez sweeps Mitra into his arms, and swings her,
Singing to her one of Rumi's sweet songs:

"Love is the mother of everything.
Love is the mother of everything."

They find a stand and buy four big Pepsi-Colas.
Mitra watches Hafez sip and asks:
"Do you wish it was a bottle of whisky instead?"
Answers Hafez: "You are my whisky. I am drunk with you."

Says the Mowlana as they sit on the sand:
"Pirooz, if you are still as puzzled by technology
As Hafez and I are puzzled by technology,
Has time not changed man at all?"
Pirooz focuses on the sneaking tide as it erases their footprints.

Finally he says: "You and I may have human DNA,
But we are in effect different species, I'm afraid."
Demands Hafez: "Different species? What do you mean?"

Pirooz fishes for a stick of driftwood
And on the sand draws a monstrous being,
With huge wings, and huge fins,
And wires sprouting from its huge radar ears.
The being's entire body is covered with eyes,
Small eyes and big eyes,
Some looking like telescopes, some looking like microscopes.
Instead of legs, the being has wheels.
A weird-looking gadget hangs from its groin
And its many rubbery arms and hands
Stretch and grab for everything in sight.
The top of its skull is cracked open like an egg,
And rising from its protruding lobes is a laptop computer.

"This," explains Pirooz, "is the Techno-sapien, the new species.
Bacteria inside us, gadgets outside us, and our improved monkey DNA,
Have united into a new being with a sharp mind but a blunted heart,
Banishing Mother Nature to a refugee camp in faraway Oblivion."
His voice is suddenly devoured by the boom of a streaking jet,
Cutting the blue sky in half with a shiny white line.
He lifts his stick and points to the plane.
"Techno-sapiens fly higher and faster than any bug or bird,
And dive deeper and swim more swiftly than any squid or fish.
They run quicker and pounce more ferociously than any cat.
Techno-sapiens can still hear the birth cry of the universe,
The Big Bang,
And see what no eagle can see, the invisible viruses nearby,
Inexistent stars dusted and lost in space and time.
No longer content with the real space they inhabit,
Techno-sapiens have invented a new habitat called Cyberspace,

Where they can work and play and make love,
Duplicating their pleasures, doubling their misery,
With a double-click of a Techno-mouse.
Use cyber as a prefix, and ism as a suffix,
And keyboard any word you want in between,
And behold the new vocabulary! Behold the new reality!
Cyber-capitalism, Cyber-eroticism, Cyber-anything-you-wishism!

"In the cyberhood the world is one neighborhood.
Open a cyberwindow and the moon is at your fingertips,
Comets zoom past your nose like happy Chevrolets.
The world of gears and gauges and gizmos is ending.
The world of assembly line-tending is ending.
The world of bits and bytes and digitized data,
Of uploading and downloading,
Is overloading our minds and congesting our senses.
The flow of info in cyberspace is linked to the flow of goods in realspace.
Buy a candy bar in Brooklyn and the electronic ripple makes
The mouth of a bean-counter in Bangkok salivate!
Darwin's bio-evolution is evolving into e-volution:
E-mail, e-commerce, e-trade, everything e-maginable.
The telephone and TV—as amazing as you think they are—
Are simply pre-history to the new e-history.
Your world is gone, mine is going, and Mitra's is emerging."

Pirooz, pausing for fresh air and fresh thoughts,
Shakes the Pepsi-Cola bottle and watches
The gas bubbles swirl like happy Dervishes.
"Rumi Jaan, you wanted to know what the brain is?
What technoscience is? And how and why the two
Reside side by side inside the swelling skull of Techno-sapiens?
Here is my answer to your question of questions:
The brain is a creative machine that rewires and revamps itself,
Day by day, experience by experience.

197

Technology is a new limb, a virtual limb,
Reaching for and grasping things once thought impossible.
A brain invents a new technology and the new technology
Seduces other brains to come around and get along!
It forces even that God of yours to come around and get along!
Once your God could snap His fingers
And somebody sick was somebody dead.
Now technology makes God wait and wait, sometimes for years,
For the soul it wants in Heaven or Hell right now!"
Rumi laughs: "Pirooz, will you please stop calling that
Mystical beauty up there *my* God? He is also *your* God!"
Rumi's eyebrows now sink low over his eyes, and he adds,
"Professor, I hope your technology is not the Devil in disguise."
It is Pirooz's turn to laugh: "If your God is also my God,
Then *my* technology is also *your* technology!"
"Pirooz, please!" Mitra begs, "Finish your lecture
So the towtruck can come to our rescue."
"My lecture is not keeping the towtruck away," Pirooz says wryly.
"It is Rumi Jaan's questions."
They all laugh now and Pirooz continues:
"At some point man said,
'The world is good, but not good enough for me.
And evolution is a good turtle, but not fast enough for me!
So I will redesign all genes, causing a revolution in evolution,
And evolutions in the revolutions, and change the essence of all beings,
Technology embodying my soul and my soul embodying technology.'
So, my friends, just as Homo-erectus disappeared,
So, too, will Homo-sapiens disappear,
Into an unimaginable artificial environment."
As if a bogey man is hiding under the bed,
All four of them quietly chant:
"And I'm not saying anything about tapwater, gas, and electricity!
The great techno-trinity of techno-civility!"

They uneasily check their watches for the time,
And uneasily check the horizon for the towtruck.
Mitra finally asks Pirooz this: "Nature gave birth to Man,
What will Man now give birth to?"
Pirooz shrugs: "I'm afraid we could become robots, like ants,
but de-socialized unlike ants.
But clearly a future unhappy for us will happen to us
Unless we design a happy future to happen to us."
Rumi rubs his woolly chin: "What pray-tell comes next?"
Pirooz ponders the question, saying finally,
"Techno-sapiens cannot change the laws of physics or chemistry,
But they can manipulate them for purposes good or bad.
So, the next thing for Techno-sapiens to do is create soft machines,
That can think, feel, and even question their creators.
Learning how imperfect their creator is,
These new machines may in despair self-genocide.
Or they may become constructive,
And fix all the defective genes inherited from Adam and Eve."
Says Hafez: "I think we must inject a little soul and love
Into this Techno-science of yours, Pirooz."

Rumi watches the waves creep toward the Techno-sapien in the sand.
A full hour has passed and still the towtruck has not come.
"If all you say is true, Pirooz, is the identity of Man in danger?"
Pirooz is lying flat, hands behind his head,
Fine crystals of sand coating his clothes like sugar on a donut.
"The danger," he says, "is not in our identity changing,
But in what our identity is changing to.
Evolution bemoans that life has only one mother
But diversity has one father after another.
The identity of everything is liquid,
Mixing with things, with ideas, flowing in time and space.
Even God's identity is formed and reformed by history.

And now genetics can change DNA, intelligence, character, and looks.
Soon the mad-genius gods of Silicon Valley
Will find a way to pop computer chips into our skulls
So that taste, ideology and knowledge can be downloaded directly
Into our willing or unwilling brains.
The individual will no longer be a cog in a machine,
But an electronic image in someone else's virtual reality—
A being incapable of dardedelling even with himself."

Rumi is puzzled: "What do you mean by *virtual*, Pirooz?
You use it all the time, the way the smart men of my time
Used the word *virtue* all the time, as if all agreed on its meaning."
"To me," answers Pirooz, "virtual things
Are *possibilities* lurking within the world of the actual.
For example, Mankind is a virtual Godkind."

The sneaking tide pounces on shore and erases
The sandy wheels on the Techno-sapien's legs.
Pirooz grabs his stick and redraws them.
"Unfortunately, Techno-sapiens are the children of greed,
As well as the children of man, producing technology that hurts."
Hafez fully agrees: " How true! Atom bombs that destroy entire cities!
Alarm clocks that destroy a good night's sleep!
Why, dear Pirooz, is this so?"
Answers Pirooz: "The story is long, but in short, it is money.
If God skimps on your breasts, a doctor will blow them up bigger.
If your muscles are too small, inject a little of this.
If your belly is too big, this machine sucks out the fat.
If your kidneys fail, find a poor man and buy one of his.
Already people are shaking hands with someone's else's hand.
How long before we will be shaking someone else's head?
All of this with few ethical standards, or much wisdom exercised.
Without qualms for fairness, cost, or consequences.
We are living longer, yes,

But paying so much attention to our images and so little to our souls,
We are becoming detached, deranged, and dreadfully unfulfilled.
We soothe our troubles with Prozac,
Which unfortunately rewires our brains.
It *prozacs* us to do what we don't want to do
And it *prozacs* us not to do what we want to do.
If we keep messing with our minds, even Mother Nature
Will need Prozac, even God!"
Mitra smiles bitterly: "I actually took Prozac for a while,
When my parents felt it would help their divorce."
Before her emotions can find a crack in the wall built around her pain,
She playfully chastises Pirooz for his solemn thoughts.
"I know life is no day at the beach,
But can't we have just one day at the beach?"

Pirooz apologizes: "I know your ears are as sore as my throat,
But please let me unburden my mind just a little bit more,
For Rumi and Hafez to know what is going on.
The antibiotics designed to digest bad bacteria—the biotics—
Are now being digested by super bacteria touristing about in jumbo jets,
Digesting whatever they want and wherever they choose.
Man, I'm afraid, will never, never master germs,
Just as the Holy Book God will never master man,
That super germ digesting earth as if it were a moldy peach."

Digesting Pirooz's words, Rumi whispers sadly:
"Now I see the face of evil whichever way I turn."

They walk up the beach and down the beach,
Until they are standing where they started,
By the drawing of the Techno-sapien,
Now largely eaten by the nibbling tide.
Says Pirooz: "One of the biggest problems of technology

Is the digestion of quality by quantity."
Asks Hafez: "But all technology is not bad, is it, Pirooz?"
"No. But it is not all good either—it depends and it all depends."
Says Mitra: "Even the unexamined technology is the ally of women!
Long before man made robots of wire and tin
He made robots of his genetically closest kin—
His daughters, his mothers, and his wives—
And programmed them to say nothing important
While dutifully doing jobs that are important.
Pirooz, the technology you deride and diminish
Has freed women to flourish and finish
The unfulfilled promise of *human* kind.
This robot-me, yes me, is rebelling!
Hafez Jaan, you had better know this about me:
I will be no one's charming cup-bearer.
I am not Layla waiting in her tent forever.
Had she a telephone, she could have called Majnun and said,
'Stop your wandering and your crying!
Come and make off with me. Come and make love to me.'
Pirooz, I agree with most all you say.
Yet you see technology as a potentially troublesome toy,
While I see it as a feminist tool—
Except for weapons, super germs, and pollutants, of course—
To free both genders from daily toil,
So we may spend our precious days achieving the vasal
You men think only exists inside your poems and dreams. "

Hafez, beaming, turns to Pirooz.
"You can see why I fell instantly in love with her!
She is the beautiful modernity I always sought."
Mitra playfully spins him around, nearly drilling him into the sand.
"Then, my love, you'd better start composing poems on the matter!
And you, too, Mowlana! What have you written that is new?
All art is persuasive somehow, and all artists philosopher kings.

There can be no neutrality, no sitting on a velvet fence.
Modern life, modern ideas, modern miseries and dangers
Require the serious attention of souls like you.
Who else but artists like you can awaken souls like me,
To question and retrain our unexamined consciousness?"
"Mitra," Hafez declares, "Now you sound like Pirooz!"
"No more than Pirooz sounding like Pirooz," she says.
They hear a rumble and see a towtruck coming,
Exactly two hours after Pirooz was promised
It would take just an hour or two.
A man with grease on his nose pours two gallons of gas in the tank,
And after a sputter or two, the taxi roars to life and begs to go home.
"You see," says Mitra, "I knew we were simply out of gas."

Says Mitra: "Sadly it was technology and not nature
That we bathed in today—let's go home."
Answers Pirooz as they walk to the cab:
"That is the worst thing about technology.
It drives man far and wide from the heartbeat of Mother Earth,
And loses him repeatedly in a universe
With infinite centers and no circumference."
Rumi grins and pushes Pirooz toward the taxi.
"Do not even begin this debate, professor,
Unless you want to walk back to Manhattan.
My God, as you call Him,
Has punished us enough for Hafez's blasphemy.
Let's not be punished even more for yours!"

They pile into the taxi and search for the highway home.
No one feels like talking, freeing their ears to focus
On the lullaby hum of the spinning tires.
Rumi folds his arms and closes his eyes,
Happy that their tumultuous day seems to be ending without

Further interference by the police, technology, or Almighty God.
He thinks of Pirooz's drawing in the sand,
And the tide slowly tickling it away.
"Before your Techno-sapiens try to build
This marvelous abacus, this computer of all computers,
To compute the beginnings and endings of everything,
Don't you think they should first discover
A machine that manufactures more wisdom?"
Adds Hafez: "And a machine to make sure love
Ascends beyond all other interests?"
And Mitra says: "And a machine that parcels out
Freedom and justice equally, regardless of labels given to people."
Pirooz bangs the taxi's roof, as if it were a timpani.
"Of course! Of course! All hope is not lost, my friends.
Compared to what will be done, nothing is done yet,
Neither the worst nor the best.
But what Techno-sapiens can achieve is as wide as all existence,
As long as all eternity, as deep as anybody's guess.
Will this new species deconstruct itself—Big Bang itself—
Back into the lifeless stuff of stars?
Or will it leap beyond inventing things and invent a new spirit,
And reconstruct itself into the immortal stuff Rumi calls God?
But as for me, my dearest friends,
I will keep healing and repairing me,
And heal and repair others as I can, and keep on loving,
Or I will die before I die."

Before entering the tunnel to Manhattan,
Hafez pats the steering wheel and says,
"Thank you my dear metal donkey,
We had such fun today because of you."
As the taxi emerges from the tunnel, Pirooz says,
"I was too unkind to New York before,

I missed it every minute we were away.
Just look at the World Trade Center there,
Those two magnificent giants kissing the stars,
Filled with people of all races, nationalities, and faiths working together.
They remind me of two tall cactuses I once met!
This city of so many dishes is the supreme table
For both the best and worst of modernity—I love it!"

16 The Engagement Party

No longer refugees, Hafez and Mitra bathe
In the desirous cool of a late-summer pond.
The crystal water twines between Mitra's breasts, which
Like exotic fish with pink nipples, float on the glistening ripples
As though needing to breathe.

Their smoldering love, rekindled to a flare by the end of their ordeal,
By the unity of their spirits and their bodies,
And by the innocent nudity of nature,
Is no longer their love alone.
It is a flaring treasure, a possibility made human for all humanity.

The pond caresses them with its intoxicating fingers,
And makes liquid love to their togetherness.
In the trees wild canaries serenade them,
And a playful wind showers them
With rose petals and divine fragrances.
And the quasars eye them from the farthest distances,
Winking with the greatest curiosity, amazement, and pleasure.

Mitra holds Hafez tightly and whispers to him:
"We are in paradise my love,
And I hold our child within me, between us, for me and for you,
And for the tree of life, which with each new reaching limb
Grows ever deeper roots.
Our child will not be shackled by indoctrination and falsehood,
By this dogma and that, that snare souls in their traps,
Littering all history and all geography
With poisons of guilt, despair and conflict.

We will see to it that our child respect the self and self-realizes."
Hafez kisses her gently on each shoulder.
"How is it that your swelling belly
Keeps me farther away from you, yet draws me so much closer?"

The child inside Mitra kicks and the pond trembles with joy.
A lily floats to Hafez and he plants it in Mitra's cupping palm.
He hugs her with his soul and kisses her with a silent poem.
Then he puts his hand over her belly and says:
"Thank you, Mitra Jaan—in you I find my dream,
In your love I find love, in your eyes I find hope,
In your harp I hear my name.
Your womb not only cradles my child, it also cradles me,
And gives birth to me.
I am reborn again and again it seems."
Mitra holds him tighter. "Hafez Jaan, say no more,
Or I will cry with joy."
Answers Hafez: "Let us cry together,
Let our tears join the ripples,
Which are so shamelessly playing with your nipples!"

The rhyme makes Mitra giggle,
And her giggle makes Hafez giggle.
Who knows where this merriment might lead
If they didn't suddenly see a man waving
From the high reeds on the opposite shore.
Mitra sinks to her neck and scolds Hafez.
"You said no one would find this pond."

Hafez rubs his frowning eyes.
"He is not exactly no one."
"You know him, Hafez Jaan?"
"He used to bring me ideas, Mitra Jaan.
So stay put my love, I will soon be back my love."

Hafez wades to shore,
Unashamed by his dripping nakedness.

The man greets him: "Hafez! You are looking well
For a man dead for six hundred years."
"Gabriel," inquires Hafez with worry, "What are you doing here?"
"Carrying out my assignment, of course!" says the archangel.
Remember, I am God's messenger.
But Hafez, what are *you* doing here?"
"I, too, am doing my assignment—being in love.
Remember, I am Hafez!"
Gabriel studies Hafez's shining young body
From naked head to naked toe.
"I thought you were supposed to be counting stars with Rumi."
"I was," says Hafez. "And I was content to do so.
But one day a heart began beating inside my cactus skin,
Reawakening my thirst for new possibilities."
Gabriel raises a single eyebrow: "And so you took matters
Into your new palpitating heart?"

Hafez waves at Mitra and she waves back.
"Gabriel, I grew tired of being a cactus,
Grew tired of counting and counting away.
It was as weary and purposeless as the long sentence I got in heaven
With nothing to do but watch virgins pass by,
Virgins that remain perpetually virgins no matter what.
If God knows it all, why should I count the stars?
I plead for a reprieve—for me and Rumi and the patient stars!"
The archangel grows stern, and noticeably more solid.
"It seems you have already reprieved yourself!"
"No, no," the poet pleads, "the possibility
of my resurrection was God's will, I am sure of it,
I took advantage of that *possibility* and here I am!"
Says Gabriel: "Wise up, Hafez! Stop this silly Pirooz possibility talk.

Who said death was a holiday? Or a honeymoon?
Who said that what's possible is also admissible?
God granted you a leave from death to refresh your spirit,
So you could resume counting stars contentedly,
Not so you could deny His wish and play Adam and Eve again."
"But Gabriel," cries Hafez, "Star counting is so boring!"
The archangel's hazy eyes flash like clouds before a storm.
"God prefers the word *peaceful*."
Answers Hafez: "Death with its abundant love is boring,
And life without abundant love is boring.
Gabriel Jaan, I beg you, tell God enough of boring things!"

"Hafez Jaan, I repeat: speak not like that rebellious Pirooz!
Speak not of what God must do!"
Then Gabriel smiles, and finds the stump of a tree,
And settles on it like an anxious fog.
"Hafez Jaan," he says. "You have always been a good friend to me.
Do you mind if we dardedel a bit?"
Hafez is aching to rejoin Mitra.
He wants to forget about his deal with God.
"Of course we can dardedel, Gabriel Jaan.
But I pray it is not a long one—my love is waiting for me."

Gabriel nods and begins: "To tell you frankly, I am bored myself.
In the old days I used to advise prophets and saviors,
To herald the coming of great truths,
To put into action the most incredible events!
Now I am a TV set, a radio, a magazine sold on the street.
Now I shout what deodorant to buy and
Which hamburger has the thicker slice of cheese!"
Hafez sympathizes with him: "You also sound like Pirooz.
But it is not your fault, nor even God's I suppose.
If your messages are all for profit, small and cynical,
It is because man has grown small and skeptical.

But find happiness where you can, Gabriel Jaan—
You still have me and my love to keep you busy!"
Gabriel ponders the poet's words,
Then shakes them off as if they were fleas.
"What am I to tell God when God wakes up, Hafez?
Are you going to resume counting stars or not?"
Hafez shakes his fist defiantly: "I am finished with counting!
I know now that counting the stars one by one is goose chasing,
Just as repeating an unprovable who-is-who prayer
Five times a day is, as Pirooz says, *self-brainwashing*.
I long to learn modern science and love modern Mitra.
Gabriel, do not get me wrong: I do not want to be wrong.
I am not complaining about God's choices for me being wrong.
But I was clearly born in times filled with wrong,
Where I had to learn too much stuff that was wrong,
And suffer from rules that were wrong and from loves that were wrong.
I want to make up for these wrongs,
To make myself free from all these wrongs."
Says Gabriel: "It sounds reasonable to me—but then *I* may be wrong."

Hafez watches Mitra waving for him to return.
But he cannot return, not just yet.
"Gabriel, blow your heavenly horn!
Let everyone here or in the hereafter know,
That by the authority of love and truth and justice,
I am going to stay in this world, and do some good in this world.
Why, why, angel of angels, am I Hafez in this world,
If God does not want me in this world?"

Gabriel sees that Hafez is adamant, that his mission has failed.
He whispers: "God bless you, Hafez Jaan."
"And God bless you, Gabriel Jaan."
They smile sadly at each other,
And just as quickly as Gabriel did appear, Gabriel has disappeared.

Hafez turns and starts back into the pond,
And with the suddenly cold water sucking at his knees,
Sees that Mitra, too, has disappeared.
He screams her name, "Mitra! Mitra! Mitra!"
And his echoes scream in a vast emptiness,
In a chilled emptiness, in a tragic emptiness,
As if the universe were only a frozen emptiness.

The screaming Hafez wakes up dreaming Hafez.
He sits and finds himself on Pirooz's sofa.
"Mitra, Mitra, Mitra," he whispers.

The three Persians say hello to the morning
With a traditional Persian breakfast:
Eggs, feta cheese, lentils, and bread,
Pistachios, melon, and a mountain of fruit.
Pirooz pours them tea from a samovar, which in the Sunday sun
Looks like a corpulent soldier strutting his brass.

"I had a dream last night," Hafez confides,
"A harrowing dream in which Gabriel appeared."
While Rumi and Pirooz eat and sip, he recounts every word,
Every image, every color, every sound, every smell.
When he is finished there are tears in his eyes,
Repeating and repeating, "And Mitra was gone, and Mitra was gone."

Rumi stands up slowly, and whirls round the table,
His head hanging, as if searching for something on the ground.
His pale voice barely reaches the ears of his companions.
"The meaning is clear, Hafez Jaan.
God wants us back in the desert.
He disapproves of our human skins and the new lives we live.
He is unhappy that his uncounted stars are waiting and waiting.

Pirooz is saved from suicide—we must go back, we must go back."
Hafez, too, is pale. "But this is absurd! I am not done here!"
"Love of God overcomes absurdity," says Rumi in return.
"We must go back to the desert, before God recalls us to death."
Pirooz speaks up: "Rumi Jaan, with all due respect I beg to differ.
Dreams are about the here, not the hereafter."
Rumi sits down and pops the shell of a fat green pistachio.
He chews it slowly, as if it's his last.
"Yes, of course, but in this case the dreamer is from the hereafter."
Hafez is defiant: "I have read all of Pirooz's books,
Frontward and backward, including various theories of dreams,
Before Freud and after Freud.
None claim that God communicates in nightmares."
Rumi glowers at him: "Out with reasons and theories, both of you.
God's will requires no substantiation or justification."

Says Pirooz, feeling insulted,
"Science is not heresy, not for picking and choosing.
Theories unfalsified apply to all cases with no exception.
The Holy Books are silent on so many subjects,
And fail to prove the things they claim true.
But science, sweet science, though still young and developing,
Is the only means to knowing."

Hafez slaps his hands on the table.
"Yes! It is better to know through science
Than to believe in old superstitions passed on as God's word."
Rumi is upset with his old friend:
"The beliefs that served you through sixty years of life,
And through centuries of death, are now merely superstition?"
"No," protests Hafez. "I simply refused Gabriel's request in my dream,
And he departed, wishing me well.
Gabriel knows, and God knows, that I will be a father soon."
He pauses now, and lights the room

212

With the diamonds sparkling in his eager eyes.
"Is my wish to live in the modern world a sin?
Is my wish to love Mitra a sin?
Is my wish to raise my child a sin?
Is my wish to wish a sin?
Believe what you will, Rumi Jaan,
And scold me as you will, Rumi Jaan,
But Gabriel's words in my dream
Were words created by my dream."

Rumi sadly reaches for Hafez's hands. "I hope that I am wrong."
Pirooz intervenes: "Mowlana, you need not pray to be wrong.
You are wrong—simply wrong."

Hafez, filled with enthusiasm, reaches for the samovar,
Pouring more tea for everyone.
"Then it is settled—my dream was just a dream,
And, if anything at all, just my subconscious putting away
My last lingering doubts and fears.
My jaans and all jaans, I have some exciting news to tell you!
News I had meant to tell you when Mitra was here.
Mitra's mother has forgiven me, and forgiven Mitra,
And has given her blessing for us to marry for real!
No more seaside ceremonies
Conducted by shellfish, my worried old fakir!
You should have seen Mitra cry! Such tears of happiness!
Tears that could bring any parched land to joy and fruitfulness!"
"That is wonderful news," says Pirooz. "Isn't it Rumi?"
The Mowlana nods sadly.

"And that is not all my good news," Hafez tells his friends.
"Thanks to you, Pirooz, for promoting me as a genius,
Columbia permitted me to take that test they call the GRE.
I did so well, they made me take it again,

Just to make sure I'm as smart as I am!
It looks like I will be soon studying physics with the graduate faculty.
Imagine it, Pirooz! Soon I will be lecturing *you* on the universe!"
Pirooz hugs him hard. "I will be your best student, Hafez."
Hafez continues: "And after our baby is born
Mitra will join me at Columbia,
And together we will learn everything there is to learn."
He is out of his chair now,
Dancing in his stocking feet on the slippery oak floor.
"God could not be more generous or compassionate to me.
Worry all you will, Rumi Jaan,
But if God had really wished me to be a cactus again,
Why would He spawn in me the possibility of all this happiness?"

Pirooz is tired of so much God-this and so much God-that.
He replies: "Hafez, Rumi, listen to my tale of discontent.
I took myself out of Iran but could not take Iran out of myself.
So I came to the desert to die, and you saved me,
And sent me back to New York to make it a home in exile.
Though I remain an accented man,
Because of your love I now understand my accent better.
Now I want to return the favor and save the two of you from exile—
Exile not only from Iran, but exile from history.
If you don't free yourselves from the past,
From the foolishness of it, and the senselessness of it,
Then, my two beloved spirits, you will not be free for the future.
And the future will not be free for you!
God is a word with so many meanings and emotions.
Unable to explain the why of what is seen,
Man developed faith in what is unseen,
And gave this great Unseen credit for everything
And the blame for nothing.
So stop God *this* and God *that*, for God's sake, stop it!"
Rumi and Hafez glance at each other and keep God's silence.

Pirooz hurries to the kitchen, and returns with a bottle of wine.
"Who cares if God exists or not—as long as wine exists.
The past is the graveyard of many gods
And the future is the graveyard of this God.
Rumi Jaan, let's you and I drink until we are as intoxicated as Hafez,
And then I will take you both to Radio City Music Hall,
Where the Rockettes will sparkle at you with their long bare legs,
Which the dogma of your time commanded to be covered.
Ahhhhh! Such beautiful long, rocketing legs,
Mushrooming from the precipitation of history,
Sprouting from the bondage of history,
Dynamiting from the dogmas of history!
Let's break the locks within us,
And open the gates within us,
And hasten backward to the resurrection of prehistoric liberty!
Or hasten forward to the postfuture, ultimate liberty!"

The next day Hafez feels himself shaking and opens his eyes.
Bending over the sofa is Pirooz, smiling with his entire face.
Hafez yawns and stretches.
"What, pray-tell, makes you so happy that I must not sleep?"
Pirooz takes his arms and pulls him to his feet.
The morning sun is just sneaking over the window sills.
"It is not one thing, Hafez Jaan, it is four things!"
"Four things?" muses Hafez.
"Then I am lucky you didn't wake me up four times.
What are these four things, Pirooz?"
Pirooz eagerly rattles them off:
"First, one of the orphans I've been teaching chess
Has just become state champion in his age group—
There is a tiny article in this morning's *Daily News*.
Secondly, my pilot's license has just arrived in the mail—

215

I am free to solo, a happy robin untethered from his mother.
Thirdly, there is your love for Mitra, fourthly, Mitra's love for you."
Hafez, still groggy, nevertheless gives him a hug.
"And I am happy at least four times that you have
Included our happiness in yours.
Now, may I go back to sleep?"
"No, you may not," says Pirooz. "I have a pre-wedding gift for you."

Two hours later the gift is unwrapped.
It is an unbounded gift, turquoise blue, hugging a joyous sun.
Pirooz's gift is the sky itself, an exhilarating flight in a tiny airplane,
High above the Hudson and the Long Island Sound,
Around and around Manhattan more than a dozen times.
The beautiful woman who taught Pirooz to fly
Has flown herself to a new job in California.
And while he is disappointed that she is gone,
He is not disappointed by the things she taught him.
Asks Pirooz as he confidently grasps the throttle:
"Did you ever dream, Hafez Jaan, that someday you'd fly?
Taste the clouds and kiss the resisting gravity?"
"Yes, but it was only a dream," Hafez whispers in wonderment.
"This modern world of yours is truly the most magical place."

"Hafez, promise me you won't be late tonight," Mitra begs,
Wishing the telephone was Hafez himself.
Answers Hafez: "What kind of man
Would be late for his own engagement party?"
"The kind who carries every fare he can," she complains,
"But does not take care to see me every day."
Hafez's love for Mitra chuckles from his hungry lips.
He, too, wishes the phone was not the phone.
"You see me almost every day at least once,
And if it is not for as long as we both wish,

216

It is because we need every penny
For that baby growing in your belly."
Mitra begs: "Just don't be late, Hafez Jaan."
"I will be so early you will think I'm actually late from yesterday."

And so Hafez begins his day,
Meandering Manhattan's maddening streets one more day,
Fare after fare after fare after fare, having fun knowing
That tonight he will have even more fun.

He gives a ride to a rich man,
Whose huge fake mustache falls off while he's crawling inside.
Hafez thinks at first this impostor is Rumi,
Keeping an eye on him on such an important day,
But the man soon confesses that he is trying to disguise himself,
Trying to visit his mistress, Julia,
For a day of sunny ecstasy, to make up
For the frustrating nights he freezes in bed,
Next to the snoring Roberta, his everlasting icicle wife.

He gives a ride to a couple eloping to Europe,
With two Persian cats, a parakeet, and a toy panda bear.
"I wish you the best," he says,
"But I fear you will spend the rest of your lives in customs,
While police check your pets for fleas,
And disembowel your bear searching for stolen jewels."

He gives a ride to a Baptist preacher on vacation from Baton Rouge.
The preacher isn't sure where he wants to go,
Yet he puts thirty dollars on the meter while
Telling Hafez how to get to heaven.
Hafez teases his passenger, saying with an earnest face,
"You make the hereafter seem so inviting,
That I think I will find an onrushing bus

And take the both of us there right now!"
The preacher quickly recognizes his stop.

He gives a ride to a nun without a habit,
And a wayward Rabbi without a yarmulke, now selling shoes,
So deeply in love, they don't stop kissing
All the way downtown to City Hall.
"We are getting married," says the nun.
"Hallelujah," says Hafez, "So am I!"

He gives a ride to a nearsighted author,
Who carries a fat messy manuscript on his neat bony lap.
"It is a book," says the author, "about those who killed Kennedy,
And all the others killed so that the real killers could stay free.
No publisher dares publish it, of course,
Because they fear my theory might be true."
Sympathetically Hafez tells him, "My dear fellow traveler,
Self-censorship, self-deception, and self-annihilation
Are ancient diseases—a long time ago I once had all three."

He gives a ride to a man with a green fedora,
Who says, "Take me wherever *you* wish to go."
Hafez, perplexed, says "I want to go everywhere, sir."
"Then take me to the place," says the man,
"Where you want to go most."
"Ahhhh," says Hafez, "I am already there."
"Then I'll get out here," says the man tipping his fedora.
"Excuse me," stutters Hafez as the man opens his door.
"You are not really Rumi, are you?"
"I am not even Persian," says the man, walking away.

Hafez gives a ride to a woman with four little kiddies,
Licking her ankles like poppies in a breezy field.
She is dropping them off at daycare, she says,

To get to her job as a nanny for one.

He gives a ride to a middle-aged lady,
Who invites him to her beach house in balmy Key West.
She will show him the time of his life,
She promises, applying her makeup, all expenses, of course, paid.
"Is it because I'm too old for you?" she asks when he refuses.
"Madam," answers Hafez, "it is I who's too old for meaningless love."

He gives a ride to two giddy teenagers,
A giggly boy and a giggly girl from some place in the Bronx.
They are too full of themselves, and too full of marijuana,
To tell him exactly where they wish to go.
Finally the girl says, "I want to fly high—
Take us to the Empire State Building,
Where the big King Kong caught airplanes like flies."
So Hafez, flying in joy himself, his happiness in sight tonight,
Ascends the elevator with them,
Wondering just who this king named Kong was.

He gives a ride to an understudy actor,
Dreaming to star on the big Broadway stage,
Where he can make the big money and feel the big love,
And someday have an understudy just like himself.
As Hafez drives, the actor hums from West Side Story,
"Tonight, Tonight," the song Mitra made true.
"May I join you?" asks Hafez, the actor says "yes,"
And together they hum all the way to Times Square.

And so the day goes, this longest of days,
Hafez ever happy, enjoying all his fares.
Finally it is seven, and the city is getting dark.
Finally he can turn on his OFF DUTY sign,
And rush to Pirooz's apartment, to shower and scrub his teeth,

And put on the new Armani suit he bought for the occasion,
To impress Mitra's mother and her very rich friends.
He is so happy, and so relieved,
That not a single one of his fares that day
Turned out to be Rumi, Gabriel, or God,
Checking up on him, warning him, whisking him away.

The night is flooding in but the day is just beginning.
Hafez in his new suit, his OFF DUTY sign bright as the North Star,
Heads for Mitra's apartment
And the engagement party soon to begin.
As he presses the gas pedal his heartbeat
Keeps perfect time with the tar playing love songs in his head.
He barely stops for a red light when
An old woman with a face wrinkled as coarsely
As the bark of an ancient pomegranate tree,
Opens the backseat door and throws herself in,
Begging him to drive her home to The Bronx,
Before the dark gets any darker and the dangers slither in.
How can Hafez refuse this woman this simplest of requests?
This old and vulnerable woman who wants only to go home?
Who wants only to be safe for one more day,
Wants to climb the long stairs and lock the long row of locks,
And get in her bed alone?
How can Hafez tell her "No"?
And so he presses on the gas, journeying away from Mitra.
"I will only be a little late," he mumbles to himself.
The bright lights of Manhattan fill the taxi's back window,
The darkening horizon of The Bronx fills the front.

Each neighborhood is poorer, crumbling buildings, littered streets.
Chain-link fences surround empty lots, sidewalks beg for feet.
He finds the right building and drops the woman off,

Refusing her money but kissing her noble hand.
When she is safely inside he drives away.
It is good to be in love, good to be helpful,
Good to sacrifice a little of yourself for the world to be better off.
He feels suddenly silly in his new Armani suit
And wishes he had time to change.

Stopping for a red light, Hafez sees coming in the other direction
A car with its headlights off.
So he flashes his lights to alert the driver,
To prevent him from having an unhappy night.

The red light turns green and Hafez drives on,
Seeing in his rearview mirror
That the car without lights has made a dangerous u-turn,
And is now behind him, following closely.
"Now isn't that strange," Hafez says to himself.

The green light in front of him turns yellow, then turns red.
Though there is very little traffic, Hafez dutifully stops.
He needs no more trouble with the law, especially not tonight.
In the mirror he sees someone jump from that dark car behind him,
And walk toward him waving, smiling like an old friend.
So Hafez lowers his window, asking, "Are you in trouble?"
The someone pulls a gun and shoots him in the chest.

Now that someone runs back to the car, and screeches away,
Leaving Hafez alone, clutching at his emptying heart.
"Mitra! Mitra!" he screams, "I'm afraid I'm going to be late!"

As his blood drains away,
As his breath drains away,
His last words drain away, too:
Mitra, Mitra, Mitra, Mitra,

Mitra, Mitra, Mitra,
Mitra, Mitra,
Mitra

MITRA!

17 An Anguishing Fire

Rumi sits glumly in front of the TV,
While Pirooz rushes about, looking for his good shoes,
Unpinning the dry-cleaning tags from his suitcoat and pants.

Pirooz is furious with the old poet.
"How can you not go? You will hurt Hafez deeply."
Answers Rumi, "He is hurting himself deeply.
Gabriel has warned him—and me—seriously."

Pirooz, finally ready, gets a bottle of champagne from the fridge,
And combs his hair one last time in the mirror by the door.
"I will tell him you've caught another cold."
Rumi clicks through several channels,
Choosing the one forecasting the weather in faraway lands.
"Tell him the truth, Pirooz, tell him that Rumi is meditating,
Trying to feel God's will in his heart."

So Pirooz closes the door loudly and descends to the street,
Hailing the first cab he sees.
The cabbie also is angry at something, pounding his fist on the seat.
"Something wrong?" Pirooz asks him.
"Another cabbie," says the cabbie, "has just been shot and killed.
"An Eye-ranian guy—I think the news said his name was Hafez."

The night gets darker and darker,
And Pirooz's mind gets darker and darker,
Until he can neither think nor see.
Then his smoldering black emotions flash,
Engulfing him in an anguishing fire,

As rage and grief battle for his staggering soul.
Grief wins at first, but rage wins at last, and
He wishes he could dump all creation
Into a giant garlic crusher and swish!
"Damn it all, damn it all," he repeats and repeats,
And joins the cabbie in pounding the seat.

Mitra hears the door knocking and runs to welcome her Hafez.
But it is not her Hafez.
It is Pirooz, pale, shaking, barely able to stand.
"What is wrong?" she asks him.
Pirooz puts his arms around her.
His tears raining on her new yellow dress.
"Hafez is dead," he whispers. "Our Hafez is dead again."

As the party swirls and sings around them,
Pirooz tells Mitra what he knows:
"Police say that the killer most likely
Was a member of the Rattlesnakes,
The gang that initiates new members
With the rite of a random death.
A new member, it seems, must be a new murderer first.
So the Rattlesnakes drive the dark streets of The Bronx,
With hearts and headlights turned off,
Until a stranger flashes his lights.
Whoever cares enough to help enough,
Is coldly killed for being fool enough."

And so the engagement party is suddenly a wake.
Fruity punch turns into bitter coffee, sweet cakes into moldy bread.
Colorful dresses darken until they are black,
Crepe paper streamers straggle like spider webs.
Laughing turns to weeping, mascara like molten lava runs.

Relatives and friends, not knowing what to say,
Can say nothing, nothing at all.
They can only surround Mitra, protectively, pathetically,
Like the grieving pillars that circle headless stone goddesses,
In the temple ruins of Persia, Greece, and Rome.
Mitra's mother holds onto the shaken Pirooz and sobs.

Mitra speaks to no one.
Mitra cries to no one.
Mitra screams to no one.
She takes a napkin decorated with pink and blue balloons,
And with a tube of red lipstick writes a note to her mother.
It says: I've no words for this world, not any more.
And I'll hear no words from this world, not any more.
For the sake of the child inside me I will continue to exist.
But do not expect me to mourn, or someday miraculously mend.
Emotion, of any sort, no longer exists for me.
Mother, family, friends, accept my silence and my widow's face.

Mitra hands the note to her mother and then goes to her room.
She shuts the door softly,
Unplugs the TV and radio softly,
Unplugs the stereo, computer, and telephone softly,
Unplugs all interest in life softly,
Except for the little life stirring inside her softly.

Too many cold hours pass before her frozen tears begin to drip.
Like melting winter she weeps and weeps
A soundless, sightless, touchless farewell to the poet from Shiraz.
Like rainy spring her tears trickle into puddles, then into ponds,
Drowning the Field of Hopes,
Until all hopes are sliding mud.
Like scorching summer her loneliness burns and burns,
And the drowned field hardens into rock,

Rock that is too hot to tread, rock that is too heavy to bear.
Like the fading days of autumn her breath grows shallow
And she falls, falls, falls from her very real nightmare
Into a nightmare that seems so very very real:

The world is wrapped in a pitch black sheet.
Even the sun is black,
And the thick clouds shed tears of black tar.
The stars are the blood-black tips of rusted nails,
Sticking from a ceiling black with soot.
Uprooted trees are black, wilting flowers are black.
Blackbirds with broken wings hop
Across a smoldering gravel of the blackest coal.
Furry black animals—bears, panthers, wild boars, and wolves—
Hobble on broken legs and weep acidic tears
As big and as hard and as black
As the blackest beans of the jungled south.
Mitra sees herself amongst the filth, below a burning tree.
Suddenly one of the tree's limbs becomes a noisy, coiling snake,
A rattlesnake, offering her an apple—at the point of a long black gun.

Mitra wakes in horror and finds sitting on her bed,
A bird as colorful as a bowl of fruit.
The bird smiles at her, a most emphatic smile,
And Mitra somehow knows that this bird is the Poem of Poems.
The magic bird hops forward, surrounds her with its loving wings,
And as if Mitra were her own little chick, whispers:
"Do, Mitra Jaan, what Hafez would do.
Journey into poetry and take refuge there.
Read poems, pray poems, cry and laugh poems,
Dream poems and endure with poems.
The music and meaning of poems are healing.
And write your own poems,
The poems called Mitra's poems,

So that your tears crystallize into memorable poems,
So that your vasal lives forever in your poems
And your loss becomes creation."

The Poem of Poems disappears
And Mitra takes the *Divan* of Hafez, and cuts out the pages
And pastes them on her bedroom walls and the ceiling,
Even on the ceiling and the closet door,
Until her room becomes the *Divan*,
So that from north and south, east and west,
Up and down, no matter what direction she faces,
Or her unborn baby faces,
They both can remember the one who remembers.

One by one the party guests leave, until only Pirooz is left.
He sits on the white leather sofa holding Mitra's mother.
Like mourning parents their tears fall on their clenched hands.
She looks so sad, he thinks, so vulnerable, yet so self-assured,
So mature yet so young, so worldly yet so meek,
So refreshingly American.

He is surprised when she leans her head against his,
And surprised that when she cries, he cries, too.
She confesses that though she at first did not approve of Hafez,
She has—had—grown to appreciate him,
To love the vibrant, kind, and humble soul of Hafez.
Pirooz wonders if she knows that Hafez
Was—is—centuries old,
And not just the young cabbie Hafez,
Who stole her daughter's heart,
But the old poet Hafez,
Who stole the heart of mankind?
Yes, Pirooz wonders this but does not ask Mitra's mother this.

If Mitra wanted her to know, then surely she already knows,
And if she happens to know, then it does not matter now,
For she praises Hafez's wisdom and creativity to no end,
His love for her Mitra to no end,
His laughs at his own human frailty to no end,
His cries for the frailties of others to no end.

It is dawn when she makes him a cup of strong coffee
And sends him on his way.
Pirooz runs the empty sidewalks, jay-running the empty streets,
Ignoring the red lights and DON'T WALK signs,
Reaching Riverside Drive just
As morning pigeons are flapping sunshine
Into the cool and gray Manhattan sky.

Pirooz had tried all night to call Rumi,
To tell Rumi about the horrible thing.
But Rumi did not answer, as he never answers,
Avoiding communication through cumbersome machines.
So Pirooz must now find the right words,
Even as his keys click open the many locks.
He calls into the dark apartment: "Rumi Jaan? Are you here?"

There is no answer, there is no Rumi,
Just the meticulously made bed of Rumi,
And a meticulously written letter by Rumi
Fastened to the refrigerator with a smiley face magnet.
The letter reads:

Pirooz Jaan, I already know the tragedy of Hafez,
And my mind cannot bear his second death,
Or to witness the death in your eyes, and dear Mitra's eyes,
As you mourn his passing.
Pray-tell professor, was it a senseless death,

Or does it, as I fear, make sense?
Did he die from the random bite of a snake,
Or was it God who bit him dead?
I have fled back to the Sonora, Pirooz Jaan,
Prudently perhaps, perhaps out of fear.
Either way, I already miss you,
And apologize for leaving you
You know that I love you.

I hope that this modernity of yours ascends beyond its pretensions,
And becomes truly modern.
I hope it rids itself of all bad gangs: bad gangs of rattlesnakes,
Bad gangs of bad businessmen, bad gangs of terrorists,
Bad gangs of bankers, moguls, and marketeers,
Seducing the innocent with the opium of self-annihilation.
I hope this modernity of yours
Rids the world of bad gangs of bad politicians,
Bomb makers and flag-waving buffoons,
Bad gangs of bad holy men, the bad guru gangs of self-improvement,
Clothing designer gangs and gangs of thieves,
Bad gangs of bad scientists who abuse science for glory and profit,
Poets forever writing the same old poems,
Artists forever painting the same vase of daisies.
Today I saw the face of evil whichever way I turned,
I, who once only saw the face of God whichever way I turned.

Yes, Pirooz, I hope this modernity of yours
Rids the world of all the bad gangs,
And brings together all the many good gangs.
I hope modernity will cleanse itself and cleanse the skies,
So the stars return and enlighten the spirit of modern man,
Uniting humankind into a single happy family gang—a good gang,
That perhaps appoints you, Pirooz Jaan, keeper of the flame.
Thank you for your hospitality and your informative rants.

Hafez and I will see you again, I pray,
After you have completed a most fruitful life.
Khoda-Hafez,
(Good bye)
Jalalad-Din Rumi

Pirooz drops to his knees
And spreads himself across the cold kitchen floor,
Wailing, weeping, shaking like a seedling fig,
Caught in a vicious Caspian gale.

18 Fear In Paradise

This morning Professor Pirooz flies to Phoenix,
With his return ticket safely in his pocket
And his luggage stuffed above him in the rack.
At the airport he flags a taxi, and to the sleepy brown cabbie says,
"Hello! Do you remember me?'

Says the cabbie with a sunflowerish smile:
"Of course I remember—
You are the crazy man with plenty of pennies,
Who went to the Sonora in the middle of the night."

Says Pirooz: "And now I wish to go there again,
In the middle of the afternoon, to the very same spot.
But this time your rearview mirror will be full of smiles,
And this time you will wait for me and then drive me back."
"You're the boss," says the cabbie.
Putting the dusty car in gear, they are quickly off.

As they speed toward the desert, like a bee toward a bloom,
Pirooz can't help but wonder who this cabbie really is.
He has learned that anybody can be anybody,
That birth is not the only beginning, death not the only end.
How can anybody's soul be fixed as a cabbie's soul at birth?
Perhaps this brown fellow is really an engineer,
With the plans for the world's longest bridge,
Burning bolt by bolt in his head.
Perhaps he is a prophet, just waiting
To straighten out man's convoluted beliefs.
Wasn't Hafez a poet masquerading as a cabbie?

Or a cabbie writing poems while waiting
For some modern genius to invent the cab?
Was Hafez always a cactus,
Permitted short vacations in the skin of a man?
Was Bob Oyster a clerk or a poet,
Or only an oyster with the talent to paint?
Who can say who anyone is or was?
Who can say who anyone will be?
Conception, birth, upbringing, death, evolution,
Are all transmogrifications of one thing into another.
Sadly, socialization transforms a born original
Into an indoctrinated copy.

As the meter clicks and the desert spreads out,
Pirooz wonders who he is, too.
And who he has been.
And who he will become.
His *I* the doer, the thinker,
His *me* the receiver of good or bad in life,
And his *mine* the possessor of belongings in and out of his mind.
If only he could renew his consciousness
His I, me, and mine,
Even beyond the bounds of his imagination,
And fly to the most distant futures
And embrace the answers to his many questions.
If only he could know what he could know, or should know.
If only amorphous time, he thinks, were a giant tree,
With real roots grinding deep into the rocks of existence.
If only this tree could be uprooted by a colossal storm—
Then those secretive roots, bared in sunlight,
Would spill all of history's secrets,
So everyone would know more about themselves.
If only the future were embedded in the tree's springtime blossoms,
Then catching the wind-blown petals,

Man would know the arriving of things before their arrival.
History hides itself, because it is ashamed of itself.
And so it cannot be uprooted, no matter how fierce the storm.
And seemingly coniferous, it has no flowers to trumpet the future.
So man is left leaning against the tree's great trunk,
As uncertain about his past as he is about his future,
Worrying that tomorrow a falling limb will crush him.
Oh, how comforting to cling onto the surfaces, Pirooz thinks,
To be happy ducks splashing over the surfaces,
Unaware of the big crocodiles below the surfaces.

"Here we are boss," says the cabbie.
Pirooz looks about nervously at the acres of cactuses and hills.
"You will wait for me?" he asks apprehensively,
Showing the cabbie a fistful of twenty dollar bills.
"I'll stay put boss," the cabbie assures him,
Producing a six-pack of cold Corona beer.
Says Pirooz, opening the door:
"Please don't be alarmed by anything you may see,
For anything may happen today, to these cactuses or to me."
"Okay boss, don't worry boss," the cabbie says,
"In my mirror I've seen it all, including myself looking back.
So, boss, your secrets are safe with me."

Pirooz breathes deeply, inhaling his expectations,
Exhaling the last of his anxieties.
He gets out, straightens his pantlegs,
And trudges toward the hill that looks most right.

A bat flaps overhead, as if welcoming Pirooz back.
And a roadrunner dashes by,
To tell all the desert's creatures that the stranger is back.
But Pirooz, trudging introspectively,
Like a pilgrim trudging toward Mecca's black stone,

Is oblivious to these swirling events.
He sees and hears nothing,
Except what he hopes to see and hear at the end of his walk.
Nearing his chosen hilltop he sees two tall saguaros side by side.
His heart quickens its beat,
Like a rocket palpitating to take off.
His walk becomes a gallop,
As his agonizing question becomes a beggar's prayer:
Are those cactuses Rumi and Hafez?
Please let Rumi and Hafez be them!

He reaches the hilltop and falls to his knees,
Struggling for the courage to look up and say to them, "Hello?"
Suddenly a sweet familiar voice fills the thin dry air:
"Pirooz, stop breathing so hard,
Or I'll be forced to give you mouth-to-mouth resuscitation!"
Pirooz begins to cry, asking in a shaky voice: "Hafez! Is that you?"
Hafez laughs and Rumi laughs,
And though Pirooz is happy with relief,
He is also shocked and filled with disbelief.
He had expected to find them covered with dewy tears,
In agony over their return to prickly skins.
"What is wrong with the two of you?" he asks,
"Carrying on like a pair of happy ducks,
When all those you left in New York
Are mourning you, missing you, dying anew every day for you."

Answers Rumi: "Pirooz! Your love for us has brought you to us,
Just as our love for you made us miss you while we waited.
What better way to celebrate a reunion than to laugh and laugh?"
Hafez is more serious: "But don't think us callous or frivolous.
We are as grieved as you and feel like crying as much as you.
But in this desert tears are dear and evaporate quickly,
While laughters echo from hill to hill.

So we laugh instead of cry, choose celebration over grief.
And laughter is therapeutic, as Freud should have said!"
Pirooz protests: "Celebration? What celebration?"
Answers Hafez: " I have mounted the impossible
Mountain of life after death.
I have met Mitra and loved Mitra,
Tasted the love of all loves after death.
I have melded with Mitra body and soul,
Achieved the vasal of all vasals with Mitra after death.
Pirooz Jaan, you still don't understand,
A moment of vasal is no less vasal than years of vasal.
Vasal is beyond the temporariness of momentary life.
Vasal is even beyond the eternality of death.
I am the most fortunate of men—
If not me who should laugh and laugh?"
Pirooz is shocked: "Yes, you loved Mitra, but what of Mitra?
She is a widow at fifteen, soon to be a mother.
And what about Mitra's loneliness?
What about a child growing without his baba?
Hafez is strangely sanguine: "Once Mitra told me
She would have given her life to meet me and be in my arms.
She realized her wish and she is still alive!
True, her baby will not have a baba,
But it will have a wonderful mother, and a fine grandmother,
And a grandfather who comes with
An armful of presents from time to time.
And the baby will have an exceptional uncle—Uncle Pirooz—
Who will finally realize the meaning of his name, *Victorious*,
By victoriously looking out for the child of the twice-dead Hafez.
And the child will love and love you, Pirooz Jaan,
As I love you, Pirooz Jaan.

Pirooz now stands still, dazed, bedazzled,
As the twin saguaros shake the hillside

With their thundering thunderlaughs.
What can he do but thunderlaugh with them,
And wonder if the cabbie also feels the earth move?
And what can he do but dance a sama,
Twirling close to Hafez and kiss and kiss his thorny hide
Until his lips are covered with blood.
Rumi, magic desert warden of every liquid drop,
Stops the bleeding before Pirooz kisses himself into a faint.
"Be careful," he tells their mortal friend,
"That the time you come to the desert *not* to die,
Is not the very time *that* you die!"

So Pirooz stops dancing and kissing
And sits like an Indian on the glassy sand,
And watches the two wonderful cactuses
As the evening sun begins its orange-ball slide.

Finally Hafez asks him: "Tell me about my Mitra,
So I can laugh and laugh,
As my heart breaks and breaks and breaks."
Pirooz pulls his knees up under his chin,
And thinks for a moment just where to start.
There is so much to tell him.
And most of it so sad that Hafez, and even Rumi,
Might laugh themselves to shreds.
"Mitra," he begins, "has not uttered a single word since your death.
Nor has she heard a single word.
Her eyes are glued to the walls of her bedroom,
To the low ceiling and the closet doors,
Where she has pasted the pages of your *Divan*.
And she has written in black letters on her dresser mirror
These words of Rumi: *I was raw, I was cooked, I was burned.*

"Her bedroom is the desert of Majnun,

But instead of the living animals of Majnun,
To nuzzle and share a silent dardedel,
Her dead toy animals are piled in the corner,
Bored with their own frigidity.
She does not play her harp,
She does not sing, listen to music, or watch her TV.
She has locked herself in, thrown her key into the abyss.
Her world is a still world, her world is a deaf world,
Her world is a speechless, cureless, and hopeless world.
She refuses her mother's help, her father's help,
Her doctor's help, my help.
When she does have to communicate,
She sends an e-mail from her computer
To her mother's computer, just across the hall.
Still, there is a flicker of hope.
She reads voraciously like you read voraciously.
I have grown a bad back lugging my books for her across town!"

Pirooz now reaches into his coat pocket,
Pulling out a page of pink paper,
Folded and folded, like the folds of a fan.
"And, Hafez Jaan, she has been writing poems.
I brought one to read, though I warn you, it is really quite sad."
He waits for Hafez to nod his permission,
Then begins to read:

"Yesterday:
Hope and love, dazzling and magical,
Danced in the heart of my palpitations.
Yesterday was me.
Today:
The love of all loves is the ash of all ashes,
As dark as unmined coal, cold as the marrow of Antarctica,
As tragic as strangled yearnings,

237

As unrelenting as a haunting thought.
Today I know not who is me.
Tomorrow:
I won't see Hafez.
Tomorrow:
My hope is emptier than empty,
As if nothing exists, as if nothing will ever exist,
As if no father were ever born, as if all fathers are gone,
As if all babies are orphaned before birth,
As if all mothers wish to die before death,
As if God tore my heart out and fed it to the vultures,
Just so He could thunderlaugh and enjoy His power!
Tomorrow is me."
As Pirooz refolds the poem he sees that a single tear
Is rolling down Hafez's quivering green trunk.

No one says a word for the longest time, perhaps for an hour,
Perhaps for a single sad minute that seems sixty long.
The sun is being devoured by the light-starved valleys
And the sky, stained with clouds of blood, is the color of undyed wool.
Finally Pirooz says: "I asked Mitra to come along, you know.
But her e-mail said she could not stand to see Hafez as a cactus.
Better she said, to go to Shiraz and crawl into his grave."
Hafez laughs a tragic laugh: "The cactus could not bear it either."
Continues Pirooz: "But she did want me to ask you
If you had a favorite name, a boy's name and a girl's name,
For the baby that's coming soon, any day."
Hafez begins to twinkle, ever so slightly, as if he had eyes.
"Mitra will know what to call the baby—yes, Rumi Jaan?"
"Yes," Rumi answers. "She will know."

Hafez now changes the subject abruptly,
As the night's first star blinks abruptly.
"Listen to my dardedel, Pirooz Jaan:

238

The only reward I received for another untimely death,
Is to count only galaxies instead of each star.
I might as well be counting neurons inside Mowlana's head!"
This makes Pirooz and Rumi laugh, real laughs, happy laughs.
Hafez goes on: "No wonder I wanted, and still want,
To turn the world upside-down and design a new world
With less grief and more joy,
And establish a new order with no scarcity of reason,
And no wonder I'm a galaxy counter in my second death.
A divinely designed death sentence, wouldn't you both agree?
Who said the heavenly masters are not compassionate!"

Dead Rumi laughs.
Dead Hafez laughs.
Grieving Pirooz laughs.
The sleepy, brown, beer-guzzling cabbie laughs.
The bats and coyotes, the beetles and snakes, the thirsty desert,
Everyone and everything, laughs and laughs and laughs,
At every silly thing that exists they laugh.
Even angels with nothing to do upstairs
But play hopscotch on the clouds, laugh and laugh.
Even old Father Abraham, playing chess with Zoroaster,
While a bull holds a lamp,
Grabs his bulging belly and laughs,
Waking The Almighty from his eternal catnap.
God rubs his holy eyes and claps his holy hands,
And declares categorically: "I'm glad I invented laughter!"

Then as the laughter in the desert dies,
God returns to his nap,
Leaving who else but Gabriel to explain that:
"God is very old, even older than time,
Even older than entropy,
And needs all the heavenly rest he can get."

Hearing the archangel's words, Pirooz chuckles and exclaims:
"Many thanks to God for inventing laughter,
To compensate for his not-so-funny inventions!"
Once again everyone and everything begin to laugh.
Even God in his dream laughs, "Ha! Ha!"
And decides in his dream that:
"After Pırooz says good-bye to his life, and all his possibility talk,
I should make him a tiny green, teddy bear cholla,
And make him stand between Rumi and Hafez,
Those two troublesome saguaros,
To count and count red ants trooping by!"
Then God's afterthoughts crown God's thoughts, and He asks:
"Have I, God of all gods, exhausted all of my possibilities?
Was I not once a possibility myself—
The mother and father of all possibilities possible?"

All things being God's thoughts
Now laugh at all things being God's thoughts.
Even the red ants that never laugh,
Laugh until they cry and cry
Worrying why God suddenly wants them counted.

When everything has once more stopped laughing,
Rumi asks Pirooz: "Have you written any poems yourself?"
Pirooz claps his hands.
"I am so glad you asked! Yes, Rumi Jaan, yes!
I've not only written some, but published one!"
He reaches into another pocket and pulls out a crumbled page.
"During the winter I went to Florida,
To Sanibel Island, to thaw out my soul.
I wanted Mitra and her mother to go along,
But Mitra wouldn't budge, and her mother wouldn't leave her,
So I boarded a plane and flew like a single goose south.

I got lost canoeing in the mangroves,
So frightened out of my wits,
That I wrote a poem about my experience.
And I brought it along for the two of you.
I call it 'Fear In Paradise.'
How appropriate for us!"
He uncrumples the page and begins:

"Lost in the mangrove cave waterways,
Of Sanibel Island sanctuary,
My canoe stuck in the mud.
I tremble as grumbling clouds invade the sky,
Tearing the bleeding sun with their dark claws,
And feeding the pieces to crocodiles' open jaws,
At the horizon beyond my sight.
Mullets in panic leap out of water,
Ospreys scream my fears to the chilling breeze,
And mangrove snakes stare at me,
Their tongues out tasting my anxiety.
The blue herons flap their wings, soaring away,
As if fare-welling my existence.
Oysters clinging to the mangrove roots fake death.

"I shut my eyes, let the nippy northern wind
Slap my face, to the left and to the right,
Prompting me to admit that I have always been lost,
In my questions, and stuck, too, to bothersome things,
As I am now stuck under the mangrove trees.
Calming down, my eyes still closed, I meditate
And resign myself to what may be.
Then I fall asleep into an unruffled dream.

"Suddenly I am awakened
By birds joyously celebrating another new day.

241

With water rising, I free my canoe and paddle on,
Finding a reincarnated sun shining brilliantly,
Welcoming the new me, and
Brimming the sanctuary with happiness.
I find my old questions and new hopes
Dancing atop the little glittering waves,
As my fears and the false answers sink into the past."

Rumi's cactus arms applaud without moving.
"Wonderful! Poetry has changed for the better I believe."
"Mowlana, you are very kind," says Pirooz.
Says Rumi: "Not so kind as to lie."

Just then the wind picks up, gathering in a storm.
The desert convulses, slinging dust into the eyes of the new-day sky.
Pirooz covers his own eyes and hears the cabbie beep his horn.
The saguaro that is Hafez turns yellow brown,
Crackles and shrieks, trembles and shrivels,
And then collapses like a leaky balloon.
Pirooz begins to pant and squeal, saying:
"Either I've angered God or bored poor Hafez to another death.
I will never write another poem again!"
Rumi laughs as he has never laughed, neither as a cactus nor a man.
"Pirooz, professor, God is not angry with you.
And, believe me, Hafez loved your poem.
But biology waits for no one it seems.
Mitra has just given birth to a fine baby boy,
And the ever-enterprising Hafez, it seems,
Has volunteered to be its eternal soul."

Before Pirooz can grasp this most unbelievable of things,
Rumi begins to moan, to crackle and tremble,
To shrivel, shriek, and collapse,
To turn as yellowy brown as the empty cactus shell of Hafez.

242

"Ahhhh!" Says Pirooz, with the widest of Persian-American smiles.
"It is twins! It is twins!"

A few hours later Pirooz is in the air, heading home, heading east,
The rising sun splashing on the plane's silver wings.
Pirooz knows where the plane is heading,
But not where he is heading,
Or where the world and all humanity are heading.
He only knows this: That the magical events he has witnessed
Are nothing, nothing, and nothing, absolutely nothing
Compared to what he has not witnessed—
The coming of being, of life, mind, and him.
And so it is, with these thoughts bubbling in his mind,
That Professor Pirooz begins the most intimate dardedel of all,
A dardedel with himself:

Now I must dardedel with me,
Wound talk and joy talk with me,
Be my own kindred spirit.
With so much hope and so much grief in me,
With so many tears to cry and laughs to laugh,
I simply don't know what to think or feel.
I know only that I am no longer the suicidal refugee me.
I only know I am going *home* to *live* and be *me*.
I must become my own star
And shine with understanding as I accept me.

Will I ever know the cause of my journey,
Or the identity of the journeyer?
Will my coffin, like my mind, brim with unanswered questions,
The questions that survive in all graves
Of all the dead, in all times and all places?

Since every beginning is also an ending,
And every ending a fresh start,
Then what song are we to sing
When someone—or something—dies?
A Happy Deathday song?
A Happy Birthday song?
And is there a language we all understand for every song?
I miss Rumi! I miss Hafez!
But are they words only, or are their words only them?
How am I to know these things?

Now Pirooz borrows a pen from a student happy to lend it,
And on the back of the poem that Mitra wrote
He writes a poem of his own:

I am a Sufi atom, listen to my dardedel.
My particles sing and sama my identity.
I'm all that exists,
If God is not made of me then he is made of nothing,
And people fear, love, pay, and pray for a whole lot of nothing.

On a cosmic journey to my ultimate possibility
I unite with fellow atoms and fly to chemistry.
Then I fly higher to biology,
To life, to consciousness, and to curiosity,
To know myself, to know the rest, to know knowing.
From man, who is made of us, I get my answers.
And *The Answer* is not that there are no answers.

Listen, people!
I've learned a thing or two on my Sufi path.
Love has many hearts, truth many ears, beauty many eyes,
And the human fate is not beyond the human reach.
Unite, dream the soul's dreams

244

And paint it with the colors of optimism.
Become the God of your own fate,
And be the sweetest smile of the universe,
And sama to the apex of unknown exhilarations.

Pirooz puts down the pen, yawns and falls asleep,
Missing the macaroni & cheese wheeling by on the cart.

19 American Lullaby, Persian La-la-ee

Mitra smiles at baby Rumi, and then at baby Hafez, his brother,
As they sleep in a big Persian cradle, a gift from their grandfather.
She is waiting for them to yawn and stretch awake,
To suckle the liquid love that springs white from her breasts.

Through the half-open door
She sees Pirooz and her mother holding hands.
She sees two miracles at once:
Her mother in love with a Persian again,
Pirooz in love with an American again.

She whispers to herself: "How enthralling it would be
If America could become what she claims to be,
And if Iran could become what she claims to be.
Then the two nations could find each other,
The way my mother and Pirooz have found each other.
Am I not a love child of East and West finding each other?
So why not this vasal of nations—this beautiful possibility?"
She smiles at her own thoughts,
Thinking of Pirooz's mantra of Pseudo Impossibilities:
"Possibilities conquer impossibilities,
Possibilities conquer impossibilities."

Nothing surprises Mitra anymore, not Pirooz and her mother,
Not the Poem of Poems just now slipping through the window,
Spreading its majestic wings over her babies
To shade them from the sunrays clamoring to kiss their eyes.
The poem the bird recites is a silent one,

But it awakens them nonetheless,
And they cry out for their mother's love.
So Mitra gathers them in her arms and sings to them
The first lines of the lullaby she has written for them,
Calling it "A Lullaby for Awakening Stars":

"Baby Hafez,
Baby Rumi,
It's time to wake up my stars
And rest on my knee.
It's time to suckle
My Milky Way wine,
Brewing inside me
Since the first day of time."

As the babies find her breasts and feast,
The enchanted bird flaps from the cradle
And lands featherly on Mitra's head.
Bending low to kiss her cheeks,
Her lips, her brows and eyes,
It tells her with a whisper:
"Life is an unfinished verse.
I, too, am an unfinished verse, the one-verse,
The unity of the universe."
Then it flaps into the poems of all languages and all times,
And fades in the world of hidden lights.

Satiated, delicious smiles enamor the babies as
Mitra puts them in the cradle like a pair of happy dreams.
The poems of Hafez pasted on her walls,
The portrait of Hafez and her naked in the sea with seagulls,
Remind her of their glorious vasal,
Of the bittersweet temporariness in one thing and all,
In her cherry blossoming times,

In her girlish pirouetting times,
In her dream-coming-true times,
In her tragic and grieving times,
And yes, even in her imagined times.
She holds her harp close to her heart,
Wishing it were her cabby Hafez,
Wishing it were her poet Hafez.
She sings the rest of her dardedel lullaby:

"Thank you my babies
My twin parakeets,
Dazzling gifts
From my lover's sweet seeds.
Though my lover can't hear me,
My love is still near me,
How can I miss my Hafez
When Hafez is here with me?
Can stars long expired
Still shine in the sky?
Thanks to you little lights
I see they fly high.
So twinkle your dreams
And suckle my love,
Brought forth from the moon
By a singing white dove.
Lullaby, la-la-ee, lullaby, la-la-ee.

"But beware my darlings,
Darlings beware,
As you grow up and up
You'll face traps everywhere.
Traps of craving and apathy,
Traps of money and lies,
Set to capture your hearts,

Set to capture your minds.
But with family and friends
Joining souls into *us*,
We'll summon the sun within us
And shatter the darkness surrounding us.
We'll tear apart all those traps,
Burning to ashes all our fears,
Nourishing our rainbows
With God's sorry tears.
Lullaby, la-la-ee, lullaby, la-la-ee.

"Baby Hafez,
Baby Rumi,
Let me tell you a story
About your father and me.
How we played lovely games
In the glittering sea,
How we found an oyster
Who gave us a key
To free our souls
For the gift of giving,
To unlock our minds
To the essence of living.
How a man and a woman,
A husband and wife,
Can melt into one
And create new life.
Lullaby, la-la-ee, lullaby, la-la-ee.

"My sweet little souls,
You have *two* mothers,
One mother is my love,
The other your love for others.
So loving your Mitra

Is just the start,
Love poetry and dance,
Music and art,
Liberty and justice,
The promise of science,
The virtue of nature,
And the power of conscience.
And when you are ready
Call the Children of Time,
And pour them big helpings
Of Milky Way wine.
Lullaby, la-la-ee, lullaby, la-la-ee.

"Sleep well my twin babies
In Time's swift cradle,
For a journey awaits you
Once you are able.
A journey on the wings
Of a singing white dove,
A flight of ascendance
To the city of Love.
Gather questions from the present,
Gather wisdom from the past,
Fill up your futures
With enough beauty to last.
Build bridges strong and patient,
One going east, one west,
And line them with lanterns
To guide us in our quest.
Lullaby, la-la-ee, lullaby, la-la-ee.

"And when you are fathers
Be mothers as well,
Choose love over hate,

Choose earth over Hell.
Dream beautiful dreams
About beautiful things,
Watch the beautiful bells
To hear their beautiful rings.
Invent a new language
Every person can speak,
A dardedel language
For the vasal we all seek.
And listen to the poets,
To their lines that are true,
And let the beauty you love
Be the beauty you do.
Lullaby, la-la-ee, lullaby, la-la-ee.

Epilogue

Ascendance: The Possibility of You and Me

There is no illuminating nova.
There is no cleansing rainstorm.
There is no music lifting the spirit.
There is no prayer seducing a miracle.
There is only the possibility of me understanding you.
There is only the possibility of you understanding me.
There is only the possibility of one soul caressing another.
There is only dardedel.